LIVING MEDICINE

Dr. Gladys T. McGarey

LIVING MEDICINE

Dr. Gladys T. McGarey

INKWELL PRODUCTIONS®

ISBN: 978-0-9814648-9-3
Library of Congress Control Number: 2008941425

Published by Inkwell Productions
10869 N. Scottsdale Road # 103-128
Scottsdale, AZ 85254-5280

Tel. 480-315-3781
E-mail info@inkwellproductions.com
Website www.inkwellproductions.com
Printed in the United States of America

Acknowledgments

I deeply appreciate my parents who, on faith, went to India during WWI, facing untold hardships, giving me the opportunity to be born in that wondrous land. My siblings filled my life with laughter and tears and great stories. My Indian families and friends enriched my life and I got to watch the healing power of love work in our lives to form bonds which can never be broken. Although poverty and disease were all around us they did not dominate our thoughts; we learned to deal with them as part of life's lessons. What a rich heritage with which to start life. I dwell in gratitude.

My 6 children and their significant others, my 10 grandchildren and 2 great grandchildren have each in their own precious ways filled my life with meaning and hope. Through the years my patients have kept me humble as I have watched and worked with the magnificence of the human spirit as it carried people through times of severe pain and sorrow with faith, hope and love. Life is a mystery to be lived – not a problem to be solved. My Study Group partners, who have met in my home weekly since 1957 have helped interpret my dreams, study the scriptures and shared my prayers. What a blessing! Doris Solbrig typed, proof-read and retyped this manuscript many times. Dean Isenberger designed the cover, and Nick Ligidakis actually published the manuscript. Throughout my whole life I acknowledge the power and grace of the Living God which has manifested in every moment of my life.

Dedication

I dedicate this book to LIFE:

To the God-given life force which enlivens every molecule and every cell of our bodies. I watch with wonder as a pair of tiny glistening hummingbirds sit quietly for a while, outside of my study, and then speed off as they continue their dance of life. As little as they are, and whether they know how beautiful they are or not, they bring love and healing to my soul. All parts of the universe are interconnected and interdependent. Life and love are the threads which hold it all together.

Life itself is living medicine.

LIVING MEDICINE

The Dwelling Place

Preface

Chapter 1: The Basement

This chapter introduces the metaphor of a home to describe the conventional practice of medicine. It identifies the basement as the place where we can look at concepts and practices in the field of medicine as the ground on which we will build our home. Some of these concepts do not contribute to life and healing, so they need to be taken away or repositioned.

Chapter 2: The Foundation

Here we see that, in order for the foundation to be firm and solid, it needs to have the proper mix of the art and science of medicine. The physician is seen not only as the doctor but also as the patient. The physician-patient relationship is addressed. The life force, as manifested in the chakra system, finds its place in the foundation

Chapter 3: The Living Room

Our living room is the place where we allow situations and emotions to enter our home. Here we identify who we are and how we care for ourselves. We also address how emotions such as anger affect us physically, mentally and spiritually, and how we deal with them.

Chapter 4: The Kitchen and Dining Room

Our diet is not just physical. What we feed our minds and spirits is just as important. How the food is prepared and presented nourishes our total being. Our emotions affect how our body uses the food.

Chapter 5: The Library

The library is where we take a look at the history of medicine and my own personal journey. This includes the work with the Edgar Cayce material and the *Feminine Face of Medicine*.

Chapter 6: The Bedroom

The bedroom is the place where the conscious and unconscious minds meet each other. It is a place of dreams and meditation, birth and death, rest and healing and a personal time for love and growth.

Chapter 7: The Playroom

In the playroom we bring together the balance of work and play. This balance helps us enjoy a truly abundant life as we stretch and grow beyond our created limits.

Chapter 8: The Bathroom

Here we deal with assimilation and elimination at all levels of our being – body, mind and spirit – as well as other dimensions of cleansing.

Chapter 9: The Garden

The garden is the front and back yard of our home. It represents the conscious face we present to the world and the work that goes on in the back yard (the unconscious). This is where we interact with nature and our environment, taking responsibility for our Earth.

Chapter 10: The Back Porch

The back porch provides an overview. Here we can watch sunsets. It represents the future of medicine with its roots in the past.

Table of Contents

Preface

I have worked my whole life as a physician with a primary focus on the field of healing. The fact that medicine has changed through the years, along with my perception of the work of those in the healing practice, has inspired me to write this book. I felt a need to make note of these changes and bring them to the attention of, first of all, myself, and then anybody who works in the field of medicine – and, in fact, anyone who can accept that the physician within is a living entity.

People ask me what kind of audience I wrote this book for. My response is: "for people." Each one of us works with the physician within and the physician without.

As a small child I grew up in India watching my parents work with the native people in the villages. I knew that their concern for people's welfare as total beings – body, mind, and spirit – was essential to their work. I knew that the diseases the Indian people contracted and the physical traumas they were living through were all part of their total life experience and that the purpose of my parents' work was to help them live their lives as fully as possible.

Sometimes they were able to ease their pain. Sometimes they were able to give them medication that allowed them to survive a bout of malaria. Sometimes they were able to help with the birth of the baby, and sometimes it was just pulling a painful tooth. I knew they served in the villages as agents of love, caring and help to their patients.

There was never an exchange of money. Occasionally, one of the people would bring a small gift, but the service rendered was just that – service given freely from the grateful hearts of my parents. As I thought about becoming a doctor, the idea that the practice of medicine would, out of necessity, have to become a business with an exchange of money seemed foreign to me. I had to learn the importance of paying for a doctor's visit as essential to the practice of medicine. I never really understood this necessary component. It was almost as if the financial part of the practice of medicine was an add-on and not really the heart of the work that I had to do.

How many other physicians have felt this way as they went into medicine? I do not know. I would not, however, be surprised if the fact that medicine has become a major business and, in order to practice it, physicians must know the business of medicine is something that many had to learn and really had not anticipated or, on a deeper level, really understood. Be that as it may, the fact remains that the practice of medicine is a business – not just in our country but around the world and, in order to survive in this field, we have had to learn about this business.

For many years I have attempted to balance the current reality of the practice of conventional medicine with what I know is my "calling." First and foremost, I consider myself a partner to the healing process, and the direction my profession has taken concerns me. Like my parents, I believe that to have "true" healing, we must not only look at the body and disease, but also treat people as total beings.

The concept of Living Medicine emerged for me one day when I was talking to friends about the fact that medicine as it is being practiced represents a killing machine that needs to change from killing to living. I stopped, raised my arms to the heavens and said, "Thank you. I have been waiting eighty-one years for that term."

The process of bringing back into the heart of medicine the energy of the feminine, the reality of the art of medicine, the spirit of the individual, alternative modalities, the physician/patient partnership and the awareness that we are total beings – body, mind, and spirit – has presented us with the challenge of giving this aspect of medicine a name. When we began using alternative modalities, such as acupuncture, homeopathy herbal medicine and biofeedback, we labeled it *alternative medicine*. I called accessing the physician/patient partnership "contacting the physician within."

The term *complementary medicine* was used when we realized that conventional medicine limited our access to available healing modalities from around the world. *Traditional medicine* became a usable term when we realized that conventional medicine was a relatively new addition to our therapeutic armentarium, and that aspects of medicine, such as massage, prayer, color and song, had been used since the beginning of time and were truly traditional.

When it became apparent that the practice of medicine failed to address the spiritual nature of our humanness and the triune nature of our being as body, mind and spirit, we came up with the term *holistic medicine*, spelling it with an "h" since the root word was the same as holy, healing and health.

The term *conventional medicine* is used to identify the allopathic approach to healing that is taught in medical and many osteopathic schools at the present time. It is what doctors and some DO's practice. This conventional approach has led to magnificent strides in the science of medicine, involving medications, therapeutic procedures and amazing surgical advances. Untold numbers of lives have been saved. The quality of medicine that deals with disease is unsurpassed.

With this in mind, it still is apparent to me that the primary focus centers on eradicating disease and disease processes. The concept of Living Medicine emerged as I realized that until we focused on life and living, we really were not dealing realistically with the human condition.

Living Medicine says that life itself is healing and that our focus is enhancing the life force. Sometimes this means dealing with a disease or getting rid of that part of our life that no longer enhances life itself. This could pose the use of drugs and surgery, but the primary focus would be on life and living instead of death and killing. Any therapeutic modalities, such as acupuncture, that enhance the life force are part of Living Medicine.

For example, homeopathy focuses on enhancing the life force. Color, music, nutrition and dance all can be part of Living Medicine. Love, joy and balance are the very heart of Living Medicine. It is healing from the inside out.

How do we define Living Medicine?

1. Living Medicine is a life process that adheres to life itself.
2. Living Medicine becomes the reality when we are able to tune in to our own lives to such an extent that living them becomes the healing.
3. Life itself creates the medicine we need for healing. This requires "at-one-ment" with the physician within and cooperation with the physician without.

4. Living Medicine is life itself.
5. Our challenge is accessing the life force. This requires being present in every moment of our life so that if circumstances present us with illness or catastrophe or joy or laughter, we can use them to enhance and infuse that life.
6. Life itself is Living Medicine.

I am writing this book with the hope that the concept of Living Medicine will help us to merge all of the realities that are manifesting in the practice of medicine at the present time and make it a win-win or good situation for all concerned. I also hope that the healing profession can incorporate healing on the monetary level, as well as holistically, since we live in a world where finances have to be looked at and are part of the physical dimension in which we live.

I write this book as a physician who recognizes the physician within each person who will be reading it. We, as practicing physicians, frequently find ourselves in the role of patient. My hope is that the role of the physician within each of us is clarified so we can communicate with each other – the physician within with the physician without.

Gladys T, McGarey, M.D., M.D. (H)
Scottsdale, Arizona
February, 2008

Chapter One

The Basement

On July 4, 1993, I moved into my new little house that was built in my daughter Helene's back yard. Since then it has become my home and my dwelling place. It also has become a metaphor for my concept of Living Medicine.

Since it was Independence Day and although I had not planned for that to be my move-in day, it, too, became a metaphor for gathering my independent thoughts about medicine. I have lived in the arena of modern medicine since the day I was born, having come into this life knowing the field of medicine was my path. My mother, who was a physician, went into labor with me at her first sight of the Taj Mahal, the magnificent tomb of Mumtaz Mahal, which I believe is a temple built to honor the divine feminine.

A house remains a house until life has been brought into it. Then it becomes a home. Since I have lived with the practice of medicine, it has become my home and my dwelling place. Using my home as a metaphor provides an opportunity to share my ideas and concepts about this great profession.

I have written articles and spoken on subjects related to this field for many years. Although the things I wrote and said in the seventies are inherently the same, life has added dimensions of understanding and a deepening awareness of the structure of medicine. Stories have grown up around the work in such a way that the practice of medicine has truly grown and become Living Medicine, healing from the inside out. The concept of Living Medicine is a living process that focuses on life and growth, not just death and killing.

Come with me as I retrace my steps in building my home of Living Medicine. My prayer is that you can take these ideas and concepts and build your own home of Living Medicine so it becomes your own personal dwelling place.

When we start to build a home, we need an architect to help with the plans and create a blueprint. When the blueprint is in hand, we begin the work of manifesting these concepts in this world in a third-dimensional way. In building a house we have to start the construction by digging into and moving the earth. Likewise, in preparing for the construction of the house of Living Medicine, we will have to change the way we think about life and healing.

In this house of Living Medicine there are some teachings we learned in medical school that were considered to be the truth. While today I find some of these facts no longer useful, they are in the earth on which this house of Living Medicine is to be built. Some of these things can be easily shifted and moved, but others are like coming upon a great rock that needs to be completely removed or broken apart.

One of these rocks is that the practice of medicine represents a war against disease. This huge rock labeled "Attack and Destroy the Disease" can't just be hauled away. It has to be broken down and repositioned so that, although diseases will continue to present the issues that Living Medicine will deal with, they will be repositioned so they are not viewed as enemies but as opportunities to access true healing. While the individual disease processes underlay the entire structure of this building of Living Medicine, they do not represent the primary soil on which the structure is built.

We may need to break down and redistribute the Earth so diseases find their balanced place. Our focus is going to be on building a living structure that will incorporate the presence of the disease and make it part of the useful energy upon which we build. Just as in martial arts, the chi energy that comes toward us is not obstructed or destroyed but used to further the action intended for the practice of this sport.

The medicine I was taught in medical school and still generally practiced is not just a war against disease; it is a killing machine. We kill bacteria, eradicate AIDS, eliminate diabetes and so forth. Our whole focus is on death, not life, so we cannot live life to our fullest. Our language itself is against life. We talk about antibiotics, antidepressants, antacids and even anti-aging. As an 86-year-old, that one really gets me. Women talk about fighting osteoporosis as if they want to fight their own bones. If the focus of our work is primarily to destroy the disease process, then we need more and more ammunition with which to do this, which, of course, are medications.

In 1955 the *Physician's Desk Reference* was half-an-inch thick. Now it's at least three inches thick with three addenda. The more we find ammunition to kill "the disease," the more that ammunition itself can and does create iatrogenic problems that have no end, just as the whole concept of war has no end. Iatrogenic disease is ranked Number Three of the diseases that kill, with heart disease first and cancer second. Bacteria and viruses are constantly becoming resistant to antibiotics, with no end to this process. World War I was the war to end wars. Maybe it's time we started to think about addressing the disease process from a different angle.

If the patient is a spiritual being, then that patient has a destiny with spiritual influences that can and often do have a direct bearing on their health. This would mean that we approach the patient as a whole person, not as a disease. We bring healing to the person, not simply curing, alleviating or destroying a disease. Because an individual has a purpose for living, the whole person – his or her past work, emotions and thoughts – all are part of the illness that exists. This concept means a shift in approach for many physicians and individuals. It also means setting an example.

I graduated from medical school in 1946, just as World War II was ending, and received my training in medicine during the entire length of the war. I started as a freshman at Women's Medical College in Philadelphia in September 1941 and, of course, the war started on December 7 of the same year. Antibiotics were discovered during this time. Sulfa and penicillin became life-saving agents; amazing surgical procedures were developed and perfected; and our ability to repair the damages that were done to the human body during this time became quite awesome.

We also began to understand a little bit about what war did to the mind of a human being and the damage that could occur to a person's psyche. It was all around us. The news was full of it; the medical profession was perfecting skills to deal with it; and I had classmates whose husbands were in Guam and Europe. Bill McGarey and I were married in 1943 when he was in the V12 program preparing to be a physician in the Navy. Throughout those four years, there was never a moment that war wasn't part of our living, breathing life. Food products were rationed; gas was rationed; tires were rationed; every tire that you put on your car was one that was recapped. You could not buy new ones, and medical supplies were scarce. We didn't complain – we were at war.

After the war our attitude toward disease did not change. Disease was still our enemy and we were to identify and destroy it. This concept that the purpose of the practice of medicine is to get rid of disease has not changed through the years; it has become more ingrained and sophisticated. Patients think that is what physicians are to do for them, and we, as physicians, are constantly learning new ways to accomplish this goal.

In the mid 1970's, I was waiting for an obstetrical patient of mine to deliver her baby at Doctor's Hospital in Phoenix. It was about three o'clock in the morning and a friend of mine, another family physician, was also waiting for a delivery. We talked about conditions in medicine. He commented, "The problem with medicine now is that the fun has all gone out of it."

I pondered this for many years and still wonder about the statement because I knew what he was talking about. By "fun" he didn't mean laughter and play; he meant the real joy that we felt when we were working with people and contacting the very essence of who they were and what we could do to help. It is why we went into medicine.

It is the essence of the doctor/patient relationship. It is the excitement that goes along with watching patients contact that inner aspect of themselves and manifest the magnificence of the human spirit. Often, in the most dire circumstances, it is the awareness that our support of the patient, whether it is through medication or surgery or any other modality, is vital to the healing process and therefore creates a bond between us and the patient that is truly an aspect of love. It is contacting the physician within the patient.

In Donna Zajonc's book, *The Politics of Hope*, she has some concepts that I feel relate very closely to Living Medicine. She says, "As leaders we consistently move our focus away from problem solving per se and focus on how to sustain a balanced life for all of the world's inhabitants."

As I look at that statement and put it in context with thoughts about Living Medicine, I believe that as long as we are concentrating on the disease and the destruction of the disease, we do not have the energy or the focus to work with the true healing of the person, or even the life force itself – the life process of the person.

Zajonc says: "When we focus on problems, our energy is directed toward what we don't want – the problems – rather than what we do want. Our vision, like our goal, is limited to getting rid of the irritant, rather than focusing on creating something delightfully effective or even artful. The more energy we place on solving problems, the more the problems in general will exert on our lives. The parameters of the problem begin to define every conversation. It's an insidious trap, but the problem focus keeps us mentally confined to very close quarters."

We could change the word *problems* to *disease* and say, "When we focus on diseases our energy is directed toward what we do not want – the diseases – rather than what we do want – healing."

As a result, the concept of how a pearl is formed comes to mind. The oyster finds a grain of sand in its shell and begins to incorporate that grain of sand into its very essence so that the sand is no longer sand, but becomes a pearl. As we begin to see diseases as irritants that need to be dealt with, like the oyster, we can go on about our lives and incorporate the disease into our structure in such a way that it is transformed and becomes a thing of beauty.

Our thoughts are like the soil upon which we build our foundation. We need to know that what we think about and say to each other has an actual effect on us and others, physically and emotionally.

I had a friend years ago who would constantly greet a person with the statement, "You don't look a bit good." I have seen her teenage daughter come down the stairs feeling and looking healthy and full of life and have her mother say to her, "You don't look a bit good." Immediately, the teenager began to look depressed, as if the energy was sucked right out of her. This focus on what is wrong with us leads us away from what is right with us, both on a personal level and as a physician.

Thoughts are things and, when we say them aloud, we give them even more energy and strength. This young teenager would have been a healthier and a more adjusted person if her mother had embraced the understanding that to greet her with a pleasant, or at least a positive, comment each morning would have been a way of helping her adjust to life.

When I examined patients, if I saw from a patient's chart that she had ovarian cancer and then started treating the cancer, I might have missed the patient. It's quite possible that I would be so focused on ovarian cancer that I hardly even noticed the patient herself.

I have had patients who, after sending them to a specialist, come back and say, "I went to see him and he never really talked to me." When I followed up with that particular specialist, he responded, "I spent fifteen to twenty minutes with her." The problem was that he spent that time with the disease, not with the patient.

It's similar to the story that Elisabeth Kübler Ross, the internationally known author of *On Death and Dying*, told me after she had her stroke and went to see a neurologist with her son. The neurologist proceeded to address her son instead of her. This lasted for about ten minutes when Elisabeth interrupted and, in her no nonsense way, reminded the neurologist that she was a person and he was to talk *her*. If he continued to talk to her son, she would send her son out of the room.

We frequently treat patients with diseases the same way by misdirecting our focus. In Living Medicine, we call our focus right back to the patient – to the person – so the physician and patient become a necessary part of the healing process.

The rock of destroying disease needs to be broken up and shifted into the very structure of our house of Living Medicine. As we examine these old concepts that are no longer working and need to be changed in the foundation of our building, we get in touch with a deeper relationship with Mother Nature. Mother Earth accepts our plan and gives us space.

Another large boulder that we have to deal with is the current concept of how to handle pain. Pain has become our Number One enemy along with disease and, rather than viewing pain as an indicator of an energy block that needs to be changed, we regard it as something that must be eliminated. The Chinese concept of pain is that it represents a block in our Chi, or our energy flow, while acupuncture removes that block to let the energy flow. If we are alive, we're going to have pain, which means that we are connected to our nervous system and our very consciousness.

I remember as a seven-year-old child in my father's Model T Ford in India hearing the words, "*Buckshish, buckshish*," and turning around and looking into the face of a leper. It didn't frighten me because I knew this man. My parents worked with lepers and he was one of the people in the leper colony. I knew the problem with leprosy was not pain; it was the opposite. The leper feels no pain since the *lepra bacillus* bacteria causing leprosy destroys the nerve fibers. Lepers could put their hands in a fire and wouldn't know that they were on fire because they have felt no pain. Rats can chew off their toes at night and they wouldn't know it.

If my finger is cut off, the part that is severed does not feel any pain. Rather, the part of my hand connected with my nervous system feels the pain and alerts my body to the need to do something about it. If I just stop the pain, as in the disease process of leprosy, then the corrective action is not taken. Our concept of what pain is and how to deal with it presents a major boulder that must be moved and distributed into the whole living process of the structure of our building.

There are other rocks that need shifting. One is the way medicine, particularly during my learning years, was predominately male-oriented. Not only were women a small minority within the system, but they were also ridiculed and ignored as much as possible.

I went to the only women's medical college in the country at the time. While there were fifty of us in the freshman class, only twenty-five of us graduated. One of the reasons was that the faculty felt that we, as women physicians, needed to be stronger, better and more equipped to deal with the field of medicine than the men; any lack of ability or stamina would disqualify us to face "the man's world of medicine." The women surgeons I knew were tougher and more mannish than the men themselves because they were told that was the only way they could succeed in medicine.

When I started my internship at the Deaconess Hospital in Cincinnati, a woman physician had never preceded me as an intern so there was no place for me to stay. My bed consisted of an X-ray table, a blanket and a pillow for the weekends when I was on call, which was from Friday morning until Sunday night. I had no support or encouragement from the resident, particularly the resident on surgery. He felt that I did not belong in medicine and his job was to get me out.

During this time I became pregnant with my first child. The resident believed that women did not belong in medicine, let alone pregnant women. He gave me every difficult job he could, such as the long surgical orthopedic procedures that would start at 7:30 in the morning and last for four to five hours. Being pregnant put me at his mercy, and I had no recourse other than to show up without any breakfast since there was no food available at that early hour. I would hang on, literally, thinking at times I could not make it through and that both my baby and I would die. However, there was no way I was going to let him pronounce the sentence on us, so I hung in there.

Then things began to change because I truly believe that there are universal forces that help us through difficult times and even angelic beings that can manifest as friends and helpers. Suddenly the schedule began to change. Instead of being scheduled for surgery at 7:30 a.m., I was scheduled at nine o'clock and could get something to eat. The resident confronted me on this and asked why I had changed the schedule. But I had not.

Then one night, about three o'clock in the morning as I returned to my X-ray table bed after seeing a patient, I saw that the little black housekeeper, Lucille, had pulled a chair up to the blackboard where the schedule was listed. She was replacing my name at 7:30 with another intern's name and putting my name down at nine o'clock. She became my angel.

There were even times when I would get a call in the middle of the night and jump off my X-ray table to run for the phone that was down the hall. My pregnancy would catch up with me halfway there and I would lose whatever I had eaten for dinner. Lucille would be right there saying, "You just go right on, Dr. Gladys; I'll clean it up." And, bless her heart, she would clean up so I could go on with my work.

As years went by, the situation did not improve very much. In 1955, when we moved to Phoenix from Ohio, I was on the staff of Good Samaritan Hospital. The parking lot just south of the hospital was guarded by a huge man responsible for keeping it reserved strictly for physicians. Every time I parked, I was confronted by him, as were the other women physicians. No matter what we did to try to identify ourselves as physicians, he simply could not comprehend it.

We would hang our stethoscopes around our necks. We would swing them noticeably in front of us as we walked. Some of the women even wore their white coats. It didn't make any difference. Every time he saw a woman parking in this lot, we would have to go through the whole process of identifying ourselves, showing our licenses and proving that we really were women doctors.

This continued until the day a woman who was small in stature but great in spirit took charge. Betty Kilpatrick was the kind of person who had the courage to preside over the deliveries of my last two children, who were born at home during a time when this was considered risky. When Betty, who stood just a little over five feet tall, was confronted by this huge obstacle of a guard, she barely came up to his umbilicus. Enough was enough. She took her stethoscope and began pounding on his belly. "There are fifteen women doctors in this city," she said. "We have a right to park here. You have no right to keep us out and you will let us park here." The poor man had no idea what was going on because he could hardly see her under the round of his belly. After that we had no problem parking our cars in the doctor's parking lot.

As women physicians we all faced situations like this and we survived, not only because of our own inner strength and focus, but also because of the forces that support, guide and help all of us in such circumstances. It is time to bring the feminine face of medicine back into the practice. This is the nurturing, caring aspect of love.

In the process of clearing we come across other concepts that simply need to be released, like dirt that is superfluous and unusable when preparing for the foundation. One such concept they taught us in medical school was that we should never befriend our patients since this would cloud our judgment and make us unobjective. This, I believe, is totally incorrect. Some of my closest friends are people who started as my patients. Because I got to know and love them, I have been more effective in working with them. As a matter of fact, I think of all of my patients as my friends.

Another concept we learned was never to give a patient false hope. I don't believe there is such a thing. I believe hope is a spiritual quality that embodies healing in its very essence. I think we can give false information, false expectation and false presentation, but we never offer false hope. Sometimes hope is the only thing that we can offer the patient. We can share the hope of comfort in relationships, or the hope of relief of some kind, and even the hope of moving through the dying process with support.

The book *Selling Sickness – How Drug Companies Are Turning Us into Patients* by Ray Moynihan and Allan Cassels (Allen & Unwin, 2005) states that the U.S. pharmaceutical companies have marketed their products toward healthy people by using fear in their advertising techniques. This book explains in great detail how the marketing strategies of the huge drug companies have progressively transformed life's normal progression into disease processes, turning worried well people into worried sick people "... so shyness becomes a sign of 'social anxiety disorder' and pre-menstrual tension is turned into a mental illness, 'pre-menstrual dysphoric disorder.' Just being at risk of an illness has become a disease in its own right."

Drug companies sell drugs to the consumer with marketing campaigns highlighting medical problems that may or may not be real and providing drugs to fight the described medical issue. Consumers then think they need the promoted drug. When people make a direct link between a medical condition and the pharmaceutical, what may be a natural process then becomes a medical problem.

The book, *Selling Sickness – How Drug Companies Are Turning Us into Patients*, points out: "They (drug companies) claim that 90 percent of elderly people in the U.S. have a condition called 'high blood pressure,' that almost 50 percent of women in the U.S. have a sexual dysfunction called FSD, and that some 40 million U.S. citizens should be taking drugs to lower their cholesterol. With help from headline-hungry media, the latest condition is routinely described as widespread, severe, crucial and always treatable with drugs." There is a promotional strategy of selling sickness and fear. Fear itself is a major cause of hypertension. When fear enters our house of Living Medicine, it has the capacity and the ability to take over the entire building.

There is one rock that I see no way of eliminating at this time. Everybody I know is dealing with it, and we have no solution for it right now. That is the issue of insurance – medical insurance, malpractice insurance and insurance of all types, which have come between the doctor and the patient and totally taken the focus of the healing process off the patient and concentrated it on the disease and the modalities used to destroy it. There are many people trying to resolve this problem, but, at the present time, I see no viable solution.

Insurance companies must stop separating the physician and the patient. Somehow, we have to invent a new currency that is not totally dependent on dollar for dollar, but on value for value. Somehow, somewhere, this needs to be developed and become a factor so that healing will really be a healing of the total person – body, mind and spirit.

In the future, insurance is something that we will need to incorporate into the structure of Living Medicine. As time goes on, innovative solutions to the insurance crisis will reveal themselves as we become more creative in our thinking and as people take more personal responsibility for their healing process. The physician within each of us should play a part in discovering these solutions.

Since the field of Living Medicine represents a living process, there will always be issues for which we have no apparent answer at the present time. But we need to keep our minds and our hearts open for solutions. With our house built on solid ground, we will be claiming the promise in the Bible, found in Matthew 7:24-25: "Everyone who hears these words of mine and acts on them will be like a man who built his house on rock. The rain fell, the floods and the winds blew and beat on that house, but it did not fall because it had been founded on rock."

When I built my little house, we conducted a special house blessing after the dirt had been moved around in preparation for the foundation. Gathering friends and relatives, we created a time capsule into which we placed some precious things. My grandson put in plastic dinosaurs and Ninja Turtles, and each of us placed something that was important to us into the time capsule. After we buried it right where my library would be, we covered it, singing and dancing on the ground over it. In this way we created holy ground. My prayer is that each one of us, as we create our own house of Living Medicine, will be able to consecrate it in such a way so that it becomes holy ground.

Chapter Two

The Foundation

The next step in building our house of Living Medicine is to create a solid foundation. It needs to be erected according to the overall plan for that particular building, which includes the plumbing, electrical work and support structures. Plans for the rest of the edifice need to be clear.

An ideal home does not require a perfect home. Rather, it means having an ideal in the home.

If the materials used are not properly assembled or if there is too much sand and not enough cement or if there is a misuse of some of the ingredients that go into building the foundation, then the whole structure will find itself unable to withstand the life it was created to house due to this imbalance. It has taken eons of time to come up with the proper mix in use at the present time and, often, this is not what it should be.

It is also essential that the foundation be in precise alignment with the overall plan. It needs to be perfectly level, without a millimeter of discrepancy. The foundation has to fit exactly into the earth and the environment in which it is being built and must take into consideration such things as weather, heat and cold, rain and snow and whatever else nature offers in that particular environment.

As we build the foundation for the house of Living Medicine, we become aware of the reality that the foundation upon which conventional medicine has been built contains many flaws. In order to have our foundation strong, we must identify some of these and work with concepts that will help build a stronger and more sustainable foundation. Jesus said, "A house built on sand cannot stand." Much of what we have worked with in conventional medicine consists of that sand. We now find ourselves in a situation where the whole system is broken. Patients are unhappy with their care and often cannot get the attention they need. They are bewildered and confused, feeling abandoned much of the time.

Physicians, on the other hand, remain disillusioned. Many of them are unable to continue their practice because they cannot financially support themselves or even meet their basic needs. Most of them struggle with complete burnout and do not know where to turn.

In the world of impressive and exciting scientific programs, the art of medicine has been shunted and many physicians have forgotten that they are primarily artists who bring healing to the body. Instead, most physicians have been taught to see themselves as scientists, abandoning the art of medicine – the caring for and understanding of the individual human being who needs help. Science, however, can be a wonderful tool utilized by the physician in his or her work and, with proper use, greatly enhance the art of medicine.

Centuries ago, when musicians only had pipes and one-string instruments, they still produced beautiful music. But, when they perfected the violin and built a Stradivarius, musicians immeasurably upgraded the capability for moving the hearts of their listeners.

In like manner, science has taken the human need for healing, which is comparable to the human need for music, and moved it from its primitive condition to the present. We now have an instrument in conventional medicine unfound in ages past that can be tuned and used. This instrument is constantly being improved and perfected.

It takes training to learn to play the violin and a desire to spend untold number of hours practicing and perfecting this art. The art of medicine requires the same kind of dedication and time to perfect. Both integrate constant and continuous practice and a constant effort to improve.

The violin is nothing without the violinist, and the science of medicine is nothing without the physician. Neither music nor medicine amounts to anything without the appropriate audience to benefit from the performance of the art. The physician needs the patient; one is not complete without the other.

When my husband, Bill, and I began studying acupuncture in the early 1970's, we were privileged to have two Japanese physicians as guests in our home. One evening they got into a heated discussion at the dinner table regarding acupuncture. The traditional physician insisted it was an art that, when properly practiced, could be therapeutic. His colleague, insisting that there had to be a scientific explanation for it, said it was necessary to evolve the science of acupuncture. It was a very exciting meal, especially since the discussion was all in Japanese, which neither of us understood. Our interpreter was a Catholic priest who had spent twenty years in Japan. It was then we realized that both approaches were necessary. The East was East, and the West was West; the two were about to meet.

Our challenge, then, is to work toward accepting science as a tool that we can use to practice our art to the benefit of our fellow humans. What is it that allows us to become artists? I believe it is love – the love of our creator, God, who opens our hearts and minds to create scientific systems. These, in turn, like the beautiful violin, can be loved and used to bring into our lives and into those of our loved ones an attunement and an "at-one-ment." Paul reminds us in the Bible (I Corinthians, 13:13): "Now abideth faith, hope and love, and the greatest of these is love." It is our training and tools that allow us to show this love in our particular way to our fellow human beings.

Medicine has evolved more and more as a science and less and less as an art. We have developed amazing scientific tools with which to fight disease. Even the concept of medicine as an art has been ridiculed. If something did not have a scientific basis, it was not considered worth looking at or researching further. We, as physicians, were taught that disease and pain were our enemies and our job in life was to attack and get rid of them. Science became our god and the spiritual nature of the human being was sacrificed to that god.

For me, this was a struggle that never quite resolved itself. The medicine I believed in and knew that I needed to be part of since I was a toddler was an art in which science would serve as a magnificent tool. What I learned was that science gave me tools with which to fight disease and kill pain.

When I got deeply involved in the practice of medicine as it intertwines with the lives of my patients, I began to look at this in a more objective way so I could compare the science and the art of medicine. What I find is that, in science, we are expected to do double blind studies. Without these, the research is considered invalid and useless. Yet, in the art of medicine we find that no two individuals are alike, no two disease processes are exactly alike, and no two cancers are exactly alike although the diagnosis may be the same. People do not react to medications exactly in the same way and they respond to treatment differently at different times and stages in their lives. The tool of double blind studies in research is useful but not binding. It gives us information but, as in any art, we need to then use this tool as it applies to individuals and to the art of healing.

In science everything has to be tested and, in the art of medicine, it has to be practiced. As in any art – for instance, playing the piano – music has to be tested and understood. The instrument has to be worked with, as well as tuned for its sound and ability to produce the music. The art of the pianist also has to be practiced. You take the tools that you have and use them, practicing and working with them until it becomes an art. The same piano can play "Chopsticks" or Beethoven. We even call what we do the "practice" of medicine. We need to know and understand our scientific tools and how they can benefit each patient.

In the science of medicine, the therapist does not get involved emotionally with the patient. Medical school teaches us to be observant and not allow our feelings to interfere with our practice. In the art of medicine, however, there has to be deep engagement of the therapist with the patient. It is only then that the observations we have gathered as our scientific tools can be used to deal with and help a particular person. The therapist becomes part of the healing team, not just the observer watching from the sidelines.

In science the physician is trained to be a doctor. We learn how to diagnose and treat diseases. In the art of medicine, physicians need to become educated in the use and application of the training they have received. You can train a pet, but you need to educate a child. This requires engaging the humanity of each individual.

In the science of medicine, it is almost as if we are artists being taught to paint-by-number. This color goes with this number; this color goes in that spot. The design has been laid out. The therapy has to be done in a certain way. In the art of medicine, there has to be variety. There is no structure that is laid down. Artists find the creative spark within themselves and are able to put that on paper. The physician needs that same creative spark in practicing the art of medicine. It cannot be a "treat-by-number." Although the tools are the same in art and science, engaging the spark of creativity within both the patient and the physician brings life to the healing process.

I recently spoke with a neural scientist at Pfizer Inc. in Connecticut. He called because he was doing some deep soul-searching. His sister who owns a health foods store was complaining about drugs and drug companies and, in addition, he struggled with some of the definitive research he was conducting on Alzheimer's disease. Having been interested in Edgar Cayce material for years, he felt that some of the Cayce's concepts about the sympathetic and parasympathetic nervous systems and the osteopathic concepts about craniosacral manipulation might be right on target.

Therefore, this belief clashed with the approach taken by his company. I talked to him about intentions and told him what was important was his focus and that holistic medicine included what he was doing. Furthermore, his being in the center of the scientific community could bring light into that community. We talked about the concept of Living Medicine and that, if he focused on living and life rather than on destroying

Alzheimer's disease, he could continue doing the work he considered so important.

His efforts help to shed a new light on Alzheimer's. New modalities are being developed to help people and their families living with the disease to actually grow with the problems. This serves as a beautiful example of how the art and science of medicine work together in order to create Living Medicine, so that life itself becomes the medicine.

My prayer is that the huge temples of the science of medicine, which we call hospitals and research centers, will find themselves bowing to the temples of the art of medicine, which we know as the human body.

In order to have a solid foundation, we must find the proper balance between art and science as well as the proper relationship of the body, mind and spirit. It has been said: "The spirit is the life; mind is the builder; the physical is the result." The metaphor that I use to relate to this affirmation is that of a projector, which is the spirit, or the light or the life. The mind represents the slide placed in that projector while the physical is the screen upon which the picture is projected. In conventional medicine we have spent a great deal of time and most of our energy on what is projected on the screen or the body. There's nothing wrong with that. If the screen is broken, dirty or unclear, then what is projected cannot really be understood and needs to be clarified.

We have spent time working with the mind and the effect it has on the physical body. We are now aware that the mind is a pivotal component in the structure of this body. The work with biofeedback and the mind/body relationship has become part of the science of medicine and now is readily accepted as being integral to the whole healing process.

The field of holistic medicine evolved when we, as physicians, realized that, without the spiritual component in medicine, we were missing the heart of the healing process. As with the 35-millimeter projector, it doesn't matter how clear the slide or how proper the screen is if it is unplugged from its source.

I think I became aware of this as a twelve-year-old child in India when I woke up one morning, sat straight up in bed and said to myself, "Gladys, there's something wrong in this world. You don't have a friend." This was true. I am a Sagittarius and, if people made me angry, I punched them out and dealt with it in an aggressive way. I had brothers from whom I learned to fight, which extended into my relationship with other people. I thought, "I don't like the way I feel and, if I'm fighting all the time, that doesn't make me feel good. Who do I know that doesn't look at life the same way?"

The obvious person was my mother. She was the kind of person who could take anything that came her way and, with just a minor shift in presenting and reframing the situation, she could come up with a humorous outlook. When she was eighty-nine years old, she fell and broke her left knee and the ribs on her left side. My father and I were moving her from the gurney onto the X-ray table when she looked up, saw the pain on our faces and said, "The old gray mare ain't what she used to be." The next day she died.

I lived with that kind of gentle humor and recognized the difference that it made because my mother had friends all over the place. People loved her and respected her. I thought I would much rather be like that than the way I was, so I started to change. I told myself that I was going to laugh instead of fight. In essence, I took that slide from the projector that said

I was a mean, nasty, hateful kid and I either cleaned it up or I threw it away. Then I put one in that said, "You're going to laugh. You're not going to fight everything that comes your way." That changed my life. By the time I was a senior in high school, I was labeled the class clown.

The projector needs to be connected to its source – electricity. It was my connection with my source, which was my mother's love and sense of humor. Going beyond and deeper than that was my connection to my divine source. Once I made that real in my life, I was able to look at things from a completely different perspective.

Living Medicine brings together the concept that life itself needs a balance of body, mind and spirit. It is the basic ingredient on which the foundation of Living Medicine is built.

Holistic medicine is dedicated to reawakening the art of healing and to bringing about an integration and balance of the body, mind, and spirit, not only of our patients but within ourselves. In order for a true healing to take place, there has to be a re-stimulation of the spiritual nature of our beings.

There are many ways to work with the spiritual nature. There is no reason why a surgical procedure conducted in a manner of caring and understanding cannot be an awakening experience.

I had a patient in the office recently who told me that when she had very serious surgery many years ago, the young resident came in to discuss what was being done. He explained how she could help her own healing process and actually took a little quiet time with her before the surgery. The whole experience was a time of spiritual growth and beauty for this woman and a turning point in her life. It is not that we have neglected to use our tools with expertise; it is the spirit in which these tools are used. We are dedicated to reawakening this within the heart, the very soul, of medicine.

The concept of Living Medicine does not eliminate the basic scientific information that we were taught in medical school. It is important to have a solid foundation, solid in anatomy and physiology, bacteriology, neurology, gastroenterology, and so forth. It is also important to understand the process of diseases – the bacterial involvement; the body's involvement; the way in which the immune system interacts with invasive pathological organisms; how medications affect the disease process; what the disease itself is and how the body responds to it; and to know about and understand the medications that affect the disease processes.

If our foundation is going to be solid, we also need to make sure that we understand the ways in which disease processes affect our very lives. Conventional medicine brings this knowledge to Living Medicine, and Living Medicine infuses the knowledge with life.

The science and art of medicine come together very clearly in dealing with issues of the endocrine system. The medical science of endocrinology has taken giant steps in understanding how the endocrine system functions in our body. We are beginning to see how it is connected to and associated with our emotional responses. We understand the connections that our thoughts and choices have on the actual functioning of the endocrine system, just as the endocrines themselves have an impact on our thoughts and choices. The endocrine glands are neuro-hormonal transducers. In other words, they serve as the area of our physiology that receives input from the sensory nervous system and then translates that information into hormonal activity.

We know now that, with the use of biofeedback, a person can have some control over the activity of the adrenals, which in turn helps maintain blood pressure and heart rate. This is more or less true of the other glands, depending on how much control the individual has over his or her own thoughts, choices and emotions.

The Hindu Fakir can slow his physiological functions down to such a minimal level that he can be pronounced dead and maintain that status for many hours. This has been validated by two medical doctors, Alyce and Elmer Green, in their groundbreaking work with biofeedback. This scientific aspect of the endocrine system continues to be researched and understood so that we have developed medications and external devises to help our bodies in the ever-present awareness that our endocrine balance is delicate. The understanding of the physical nature and the scientific component of our endocrine system is being wonderfully brought to our awareness and our attention. In order to practice the art of medicine using science as a tool, it is important that we look at the endocrine system from the point of view of our spiritual nature. Understanding the symbolism associated with the endocrine system allows us to contact our unconscious self through dreams and visions.

Our life force has been known in religious terms as the spirit, chi, prahna and kundalini. The kundalini is the rising energy that activates the spiritual centers, or hormonal glands, also known as chakras in the Hindu tradition, the seven candlesticks and the seven churches in the New Testament, as well as Ezekiel's wheel in the Old Testament. These vortices of energy in specific areas of the body consist of seven major spiritual centers or chakras, five minor ones and others that are identified by different systems and traditions.

These seven major centers include: the first or base chakra, where the sperm and ovum are created in the testicles and ovaries. The second chakra is located in the Leydig cells, the interstitial cells in the testicles and ovaries that produce the sex hormones. The adrenal glands represent the third chakra. Known as the major energy center, they sit like little caps on top of the kidneys. The fourth center is in the thymus or heart chakra, known as the love center in the chest cavity. The fifth chakra is located in the thyroid glands associated with the will and situated in the neck. The sixth center or pineal gland is associated with light and cycles within the body and lies in the center of the brain. The seventh chakra in the pituitary gland is the master gland and controls the other glands. It lies in the head a little below and in front of the pineal. Each one of these glands reflects major symbolism that has been identified in different cultures and been known for eons.

The four centers that are located within the trunk of the body are known as the Earth centers. The symbolism associated with these has to do with four elements – earth the first, water the second, fire the third and air the fourth. They also are represented by animals – the bull or the cow as the first, the androgynous man as the second, the lion or the cat as the third, and the eagle as the fourth. Different cultures have different symbols associated with these four centers, depending on their own background.

The five senses tie the Earth centers with the centers in the heavens. The relationships of these five senses are: the gonads, sense of smell; Leydig, sense of taste; adrenal, sight; thymus, feeling; and thyroid, hearing. The two higher centers come into the symbolism as we look at the seven notes of the piano, the seven colors of the rainbow, the seven days of the week and so forth.

In her book *Anatomy of the Spirit*, Carolyn Myss, Ph.D., goes into detail about how this system works. My little book, *Dopey's Path to Enlightenment*, and Dora Kunz's book, *The Personal Aura*, offer greater detail about the functioning and the symbolism associated with these centers. There are many more books that deal with this subject.

It is important to be aware of the symbolism associated with the endocrine centers because we use it in our everyday life. Our dreams, if we're going to interpret them at all, have a deeper and more usable language when we incorporate our understanding of the symbols associated with the chakras. For instance, dreaming about a lion or a tiger provides a symbol of adrenal activity. If we dream of an eagle or a hummingbird, we are connecting with the activity of the thymus. It is very helpful in working with people's dreams to understand some of these metaphors.

A patient of mine had a series of dreams about a tiger. He was having a hard time controlling his temper, and his blood pressure was high. When he began relating his dreams to me, he first saw a tiger that was locked up in his basement and that had to be fed. He had several dreams dealing with this tiger. Then he dreamed he was holding onto its tail. He had allowed the tiger to come out of the basement and it was pulling him down a cinder path. His feet were bleeding but he held on tightly to the tiger's tail. Soon thereafter, he dreamed he was at Oak Creek in Sedona, Arizona, splashing in the water with the tiger. This dream series took place over a period of years during which he was working with his emotions, meditating, doing yoga and biofeedback, and paying attention to his diet. He was learning not only to control his anger, but also to embrace his own energy.

There probably was never a point in time when we knew as much about the body and mind as well as its diseases as we do now. We actually understand a great deal about how emotions interact with and impact the body, mind and spirit of an individual. We have research at our fingertips that represents solid science and good medicine. There is no country in the world where acute illnesses, trauma, surgical procedures and chemical intervention are as well-studied and practiced as in America. If I have a major trauma, such as a broken leg, there is no place I would rather be for my therapy than in our United States.

The question is how we can make this knowledge accessible to people.

During a magazine interview in August 2002, the writer asked me: "How should the state of Arizona contend with the shortage of skilled medical professionals?" My answer was:

"The way to deal with the lack of medical care in the state is by empowering the individuals to take back their own healing in a way that allows them to contact and work with the physician within them. They know what they can and cannot eat. They know exercise is healthy and worthwhile. The only way we can do this is by empowering the individual, because we're never going to have enough doctors to conquer all the diseases." This holds true to this day.

If the field of medicine is really going to move into the future, we need to take responsibility for ourselves. We need to stop blaming other people for any and everything that happens to us. We need to work with physicians as partners and truly allow healing to happen.

The importance of each individual accepting responsibility for his or her own healing is a major ingredient in the mix of science and the art of medicine.

Years ago I had a patient call me on a Friday afternoon from Flagstaff, Arizona. At the time I was living in Casa Grande, Arizona – a forty-five minute drive from my office. Since it was late in the afternoon, I decided to wait until I got home to return her call. Since I could not find the message, I thought I could wait until Monday to call her back. If she was really in trouble, she would probably call me over the weekend.

On Monday, when I got back to the office and found her message, I called her. She said, "I was really angry with you when you didn't call me back, but then I got to thinking: If Dr. Gladys had called me back, she probably would have said, 'What do you think is wrong?' I probably would have said, 'I think I have a bladder infection but the doctor said I have a vaginal infection.'"

With this information in mind, she went to the doctor on Saturday telling him she thought she had a bladder infection. When he said he thought it was a vaginal infection, she asked him to check and of course, she was right. So, you see, when she checked with the physician within her, she got information that the physician outside of her did not have, and they were able to work together as a team. Those of us who have the credentials to be called physicians will find our real colleague when we treat the physician within the patient with respect.

My oldest son has been an orthopedic surgeon for many years. When he had finished his training, he said to me, "Mom, I'm really worried. Here I am with all this training and I'm going out to work with people. I'll have people's lives in my hands, and I don't know if I can handle the responsibility."

Having struggled with this same problem for years, I was able to answer him: "Son, you as a physician may pull an incision together and suture it well, but you cannot make it heal.

If you think you are the one who does the healing, you should be scared. But, if you can understand that you are a channel through which healing moves, that your job is to contact the physician within each person to awaken the healing force in each patient and if you do the very best job you know how to do, then you have nothing to fear." We teach our children what we need to learn.

The foundation of Living Medicine remains very fragile and undependable until we grapple with and address the issue of the patient/physician relationship and see the physician becoming a coach in the healing process. When I was president of the American Holistic Medical Association in 1984, I wrote an article that I am quoting in its entirety. I believe it captures the ingredient that strengthens the foundation so that our work in the future will be right on line, and working with and responding to the changes that are coming in this changing world.

> *In September of this year I was in London for the formation of the British Holistic Medical Association meeting. While there I met physicians from many different countries. One of the physicians was an orthopedic surgeon from South Africa. We were talking about various things and he said something which stuck with me and which I would like to share with you. He said the motto in his office was what he called the three A's – accessibility, affability, and ability. It was important for everybody from his front desk on back to know and understand these three A's.*

The concept of accessibility is truly basic in a holistic practice. If we are not available to our patients, if our actual hours and our life style is such that patients can't get to us, then there isn't very much that we can do to help them. But beyond that, accessibility to me means being willing to allow a patient to access more than our time, even more than our knowledge. We must allow them to be part of our very healing quality, the spirit within.

Without this, we have not really made contact with the patient. We may have bound up their wounds and given them some relief from their symptoms, but until we are really available to them, we cannot work in the area of true healing. Mother Teresa had to become accessible to the derelicts in Calcutta before her mission became a reality. In order to do this, she felt that she had to go and live as they lived and be part of their whole life as much as she could.

We may not need to do what Mother Teresa does, but at some level of our awareness, we do need to be accessible at a deeper level than just a passing relationship if we are to really help.

***Affability**. A person might be accessible to their patients on a physical level and yet be so caught up with their own problems or their own awareness that they don't even understand the importance of kindness and gentleness and the qualities of spirit which separate us from animals and make us truly human. A friendly* *smile can do more for healing sometimes than a mighty drug. There are people who just by their affability help others to understand their problems and their conditions and healing begins to take place. In order to be affable, we have to stretch ourselves past where we want to be and allow ourselves to feel what the patient is looking for and needs.*

Ability. *When you get right down to it, unless we have the training and the ability to do our job, the first two don't amount to very much. In order to be a good physician in this day and age, we need to know the tools which we learned in medical school and our training programs and be able to use them in a healing manner. Our abilities as physicians are essential to the whole process of healing. If an orthopedic surgeon does not know how to work with bones, it doesn't matter a great deal how accessible or how affable he is.*

Mother Teresa said it like this: "The biggest disease today is not leprosy or tuberculosis, but rather the feeling of being unwanted, uncared for and deserted by everybody. The greatest evil is the lack of love and charity, the terrible indifference toward one's neighbor who lives at the roadside assaulted by exploitation, corruption, poverty and disease."

So it seems to me that this triad is an excellent model for a holistic physician and their office staff. We need to meet people where they are and work with them at the level they can understand and allow ourselves to be involved in depth in the healing process.

Using the three A's can bring about a clearer understanding of how to function as holistic physicians, but also give to those who need it a true experience in healing.

And again, when I was president of the AHMA the message I wrote in the November/December 1983 newsletter was right to this very point and I will quote it in its entirety.

In the September 1983 issue of Continuing Education, I found an article which was stimulating and exciting to me and triggered a response which I think needs to be spoken to and expressed. The title was "The Singular Sadness of Numerical Madness" and it was written by Richard B. Lee, M.D. The thrust of the article was that somehow with our technology and our ability to pull statistics together, we have lost sight of the individual patient. He makes a point that if we do not have statistical significance to work with, the importance of a single case history is lost and even labeled anecdotal.

This has long been a problem which I have wanted to address. Most of the work I have done has been with individual cases, and my reporting has been on my clinical observations and the results of our work. This has been labeled anecdotal and, therefore, not only insignificant, but of no value. To me it has seemed that a case history is just that – a case history.

Each individual in my office with a problem was asking for help and to each one the statistical importance of a certain disease cure rate was relatively unimportant. I'm not down playing statistics. I think they have their value, but more in the nature of background music for a play – not the primary focus of our attention.

In other words, we must not get so wrapped up in statistics that we cannot see the importance of dealing with an individual patient who has his own particular accumulation of symptoms. When this happens, the patient is left without any help and nowhere to turn.

Biblical literature is replete with information about the importance of the individual. Jesus talked about the good shepherd who left the 99 and sought after the one lost sheep. He talked about the woman who had a special place in the kingdom of heaven because she contributed her widow's mite.

It has been said that if there is one white crow, it proves that all crows are not black.

It is not the masses who have changed the world, rather the individual person here and there – the Buddha, the Mohammed, the Paracelsus, the Jesus. The individual person who was in tune enough with his spirit that he was able to kindle light and life in the lives of other people. This does not happen in masses. It happens

> *because the spirit of God illumines one soul here and another one there. Mother Teresa worked with the masses of people in India, but she did not see them as diseases or people without faces. She saw them as individual beings with a soul and a spirit that needed to be awakened.*
>
> *In looking at research in our organization, it is nice to have some statistics to work with, but I pray that we never lose sight of the fact that a true physician works with individual patients as individuals who are created in the image of God and that in reality each one of us is striving to "know ourselves, to be ourselves, yet one with God." That's what healing is all about, isn't it?*

When I am face-to-face with someone in my office, or addressing the reality of the microcosm within the macrocosm, which is my patient, then that one individual in the moment becomes truly a great mystery. And nothing in the world is as important or as exciting. It does not matter whether s/he is young or old, black or white, "curable" or "incurable" – each patient is unique and wonderfully different. Diseases can be the same. Therapies can be the same. But no two patients are the same. Statistics are important when we treat diseases and use therapies, but fall into the background when we work with the individual.

If I as a physician bring my training and my caring into the picture and make contact with the seeking part of that particular individual, at that point a marvelous thing happens. At some level within both of our beings, healing takes place. This is truly more important than the cure of any one disease. The individual patient's involvement in his or her own healing is an important part of a good foundation.

My frustration early on in the practice of medicine consisted primarily with patients who were not taking responsibility for their healing or even their health conditions. I am delighted to say that this has changed through the years. More and more people are becoming aware of how important lifestyle changes, thought processes, living conditions and environmental factors impact their well-being. They are now beginning to look at the part they play in their own health and well-being. This is very gratifying.

I truly believe that we need to be much more aware of and focused on this physician/patient partnership and the way in which everything that we do creates who and what we are. Whatever we think manifests in what is going on in our lives and in our bodies. What our emotions are in relationship to things that happen in our lives can be worked with in many ways, including body work, biofeedback and exercise, nutrition and electromagnetic field therapies.

Working with the symbols associated with the endocrine centers in our dreams can be very helpful. The impact of prayer and meditation on the whole healing process is being validated and becomes part of a person's whole healing armamentarium. We need to be less focused on killing diseases and more focused on enhancing the immune system and allowing people to engage in their own healing process. We need to work with music and color, beauty and touch, and joy and laughter as very important therapeutic tools. We already understand that molecular structure can change with emotional impact and that prayer is a mighty healing force.

In Candice Pert's book, *Molecules of Emotion*, she scientifically puts into context the reality that cells have consciousness and that a relationship exists between thoughts, emotions and the actual cellular structure of our body. Her work is pivotal in establishing a solid foundation for our home of Living Medicine because it integrates the science and art in a very usable way.

Creating a solid foundation for the structure is ongoing work and a difficult process, and like any living process or living body, it requires that all aspects of the foundation are integrated and work well together. When the AHMA was formed, "strength through diversity" was listed among the first in the list of roles and objectives. The goal was "to provide a common ground where diverse interests in medicine can find unity in ideals and values, recognizing the diverse approaches converge on a unified philosophy of holistic medicine."

We have all had the privilege of listening to a symphony in which the individual instruments together provide a harmonic sound that stirs us to our very depths. We could take an individual instrument and listen to it with appreciation and then listen to another one with added appreciation, but it is not until the sounds of each instrument are combined in a particular way that it becomes music that touches the soul.

If each instrument were to play a different tune, all would be confusion and discord. But when they are united in a single purpose of producing a particular piece of music, the result is often great artistry.

In the field of Living Medicine, we have physicians of all types: surgeons, oncologists, acupuncturists, homeopaths, osteopaths, obstetricians and pediatricians. Some physicians are teachers and professors while others include researchers, general practitioners, family physicians, neurologists, urologists – the list goes on.

The Apostle Paul said it this way in I Corinthians, 12:18: "But as it is, God arranged the organs in the body, each one of them as He chose. If all were a single organ, where would the body be? As it is there are many parts, yet one body."

So what makes Living Medicine different? The difference, as I see it, is that we are unified in trying to be of service to each person we contact, keeping the values of the unity of body, mind and spirit foremost in our work with patients, whatever the approach, specialty or situation we may be experiencing. If this is our goal, or our ideal, it follows logically and sequentially that as we do the work we need to do, we ourselves grow and we stimulate growth within others.

Because we are not afraid to address the spiritual nature of our being and open ourselves to guidance from the power that is greater than we are, we can expect to be involved in the healing process that is transformational.

One of the questions I ask patients is, "What do you want to get well for? Is it to go right back to doing the things that made you sick in the first place or are you ready to make a change in your life and commit yourself to the healing process, which means an attunement with your total being?"

If we as physicians are truly working toward a single ideal, it makes no difference how many diverse approaches we have or even philosophies. We might even be diametrically opposed in a specific therapeutic approach. But if our purpose is the same, the result will be like the harmony we hear in the beauty of a symphony.

The strength that comes from diversity is likewise multidimensional and can be tremendously beautiful.

Life has never been easy, and the living process has its own ability to stretch and make us grow.

Years ago I sat on a speaker's platform with a Japanese man who made an important statement. He said, "Hard jobs are done by those who can. Impossible jobs are done by those who care. Transforming jobs are done by those who are committed."

Notice that he never mentioned easy jobs. We, as physicians, do not have an easy job to do. It's a hard one – a very hard one – but we can do it. Because we are capable; we are well-trained; and we are good doctors. We know how to treat sick people as well as those who are already healthy and we are learning more about this every day. We can work in hospitals and in emergency rooms. We can work in the backwoods, in farm communities and in big cities. Because we are not locked into rigid structures from the past, we are willing to open our minds to the healing techniques that come from the past and the present. We have a wonderfully hard job to do and we can do it.

Because we care, we can do an impossible job. Not only do we care, but our patients and people themselves care. They care about each other and they care about us.

We have a transformational job to do because we are committed. We are bound to a standard of excellence that brings research and science in medicine forward into their proper place in the art of medicine, transforming the science of medicine into what it really is – an art, with science as its tool.

Truly great artists, like the truly great physicians, are those who go beyond the techniques that they use well and tap into the transforming essence of the spirit. They lose themselves as ego structures and connect with the source of all life in creativity. As we work with the concept that "my spirit beareth witness with thy spirit" and as we work with healing of others, we are truly healed.

Jesus said, "I have come not to destroy the law, but to fulfill it."

We have come not to destroy medicine but to awaken in it the knowledge and reality that all healing comes from one source, whether it be the knife, castor oil, or a prayer.

We are trained to bring about cures, but we are dedicated to healing. We are trained in the science of medicine, but we are dedicated to the art of medicine.

As we use the art of medicine for transformation in the whole field of medicine, we are truly transformed. The assumption that patients should be informed and can make wise decisions represents the very heart of healing.

This is the true essence of Living Medicine. It is healing from the inside out. It takes the concept of holistic medicine, which deals with healing of the body, mind and spirit, to another level. The emphasis in Living Medicine so clearly focuses on life and the living process so that the disease itself can be incorporated into the life process as a living thing. As a patient lives her life, a disease can become a part of whom and what she is, without focusing on the disease but allowing it to be a part of her growth.

When I speak to other physicians, I recognize that the physician within me makes contact with the physician within the other doctor. We must work together in bringing life back into the heart of medicine. The physician without and the physician within are part and parcel of the whole and are important in creating a solid foundation for the house of Living Medicine.

Chapter Three

The Living Room

As we open the front door to others and invite our guests into our living room, we step into the part of the home where real life starts to take place. This is where relationships begin, where our own living process interacts with others who come in and out and where we recognize our connection to other people. Our living room is what truly expresses or manifests to others how we see ourselves so we can relate to others. First, we need to really look at the furnishings in the living room, the pictures on the wall and the general ambiance of the room, which defines our own personality. If we do not pay attention to this and if we do not know who and what we are, then our neighbors and friends only see confusion and distress.

Through the years I have introduced myself by saying, "I'm Gladys McGarey. I'm a physician." A few years back, after I had said that to somebody, I stopped and thought about the statement. If I am a physician and that is all I am, then what happens if I lose my license or find myself in a position where I cannot practice anymore? Am I no longer a person or no longer relevant? If we label ourselves with our profession, we are limiting who and what we are. I now introduce myself as: "Gladys McGarey. I work as a physician," because I realize that my profession helps to describe the work that I do but does not reflect my whole identity.

Edgar Cayce said: "We need to know ourselves, to be ourselves, yet one with God." As we get to know ourselves, we can begin to love ourselves.

I had a patient in my office recently who has multiple sclerosis. She came in very excited because she had a dream to share in which she saw a little girl, about four years old, lying face down in the mud. She picked her up, turned her around and looked into the little girl's face. Much to her surprise, it was her own face. She held the little girl tightly and said, "Oh I love you; I really, really love you." When she awakened and shared the dream with her husband, he said, "Yeah, well, okay." "NO! NO!" she said, "You don't get it. I really, really love that little girl."

This woman grew up being taught that loving oneself was wrong. She was supposed to love others, but not herself. Loving oneself was selfish and self-centered. In her dream and in the waking state since that dream, she knew she loved this little girl and that it was right. She felt stronger and more at peace when she accepted the message that loving herself was good.

Many of my patients through the years, particularly women, have trouble accepting and loving themselves, or even caring for themselves. It is easier for them to deal with other people's problems and needs that are more in line with what they have been taught is God's will. They were raised to focus their energies outside themselves. In reality, this is not what Jesus taught. The central core of his teaching is to love the Lord your God and to love your neighbor as yourself. The Lord's Prayer also reminds us to forgive our debts as we forgive our debtors.

We talk about unconditional love, but one of the conditions we put on ourselves is that we have to be worthy of our love for ourselves. We know our own faults better than anyone else, so we judge ourselves to be unlovable. This is not how God loves us or how we really can love one another. Love really needs to be without judgment.

Our family had just moved to Phoenix when my son, Bob, was four-and-a-half years old. He came running into the house one day and said, "Mamma, I know if I make a friend and he makes a friend and he makes a friend and he makes a friend, it'll go all around the world and come back to me." Somehow he knew it had to start with him. He had to become his own friend. Wouldn't it be great if that philosophy permeated all of our lives!

If we do not take care of ourselves, we cannot take care of other people. A good example of this is what happens every time you get on an airplane. The flight attendants always give a little sermon before the flight begins. In essence, they say, "If the oxygen mask drops down in front of you, don't put it on the person next to you before you put it on yourself." In other words, you cannot take care of the person next to you if you do not take care of yourself.

We understand the importance of what the flight attendant says on this three-dimensional plane. The analogy also holds on a spiritual plane. Only as we allow the breath of God to fill our hearts can we be of true service to one another. We can recognize that the breath of God is symbolized by the oxygen mask dropping down, and we as individuals need to make our own connection with God.

Another example is a woman who, when she is pregnant, has to care for herself mentally, physically and spiritually. As she does this, she nurtures the child growing within.

It remains evident all through our lives that a central part of our service to one another is first an internal process of self-care and then to take what we have learned into the outer world. However, for many of us it is harder to receive than to give. In order to truly receive, we must accept the fact that we are in need. This is difficult sometimes because accepting help reminds us of our vulnerability, our humanness. The good news is that when we live fully in our humanness, we are not only healthy within but we also have greater gifts to give to others. When we admit our need, we are empowered to receive. As we receive help from others, we are filled. Now we can give more fully of ourselves.

Another statement is that in order to be lovable we must be "love-able." And in order to be able to love, we must start with ourselves. This is not being selfish; it is being self-aware. It is not being self-centered; it is caring for ourselves.

We seek peace and love for this world. We must start with ourselves and learn, as my patient did, to really, really love that "little girl" or "little boy" within.

This is a lesson I had to learn again during my recovery from a total hip replacement. I was going through the process of allowing my body to heal, allowing myself to accept help from family and friends and being forced to focus on my own healing process from within. It was a blessing to me to open my heart and receive the love and healing that was sent my way. It was a reminder of so many lessons I have shared with patients. My twelve-year-old grandson brought me the series of books he had been reading. As I healed, I allowed myself to be twelve years old and enjoy that growing aspect of myself.

The concept of knowing ourselves is fundamental to Living Medicine. True healing occurs when patients take responsibility for and begin to understand who and what they are, what their emotions are, how they feel about things, as well as how they respond to change in their lives. They have to decide whether they want to keep the windows closed and the blinds down, or whether they are willing to open the windows wide and let the light shine in.

We must know what we want in our living room – the true dwelling place where we get to tell our own story.

In 2005 I spent three months in northern India and Afghanistan. My visit to Afghanistan was particularly important because of the stories I heard from individual women. Thirty women from ten different villages in the remotest part of the Bamian District gathered together in the "living room" of a house where we held a weeklong conference for mothers-in-law.

Initially, we had to get permission from the men of these villages prior to even considering the possibility of working with their women. At first the men objected, saying they did not want their women away from the home. They feared what they would be exposed to since women in Afghanistan are not permitted to show their faces to any man except those within their immediate family. When we explained that we wanted to talk to their mothers-in-law instead of their wives and daughters, they agreed for reasons we really don't understand. We wanted to meet with these women because they were mature, with stories to share that had never been told. No one listened to them because their stories were not considered important.

As we sat around on the floor in this living room, woman-to-woman, and told our stories, the living essence of healing could be felt the whole time. What we learned within this gathering is presented later on in this book. The experience brought out their pain, their joy, their fears and their hopes as they shared their pregnancy histories with us. As the women communicated with each other, it helped us understand more about the illnesses they faced.

One physician friend describes illness as "social communication" – a socially acceptable way of letting ourselves and those around us know that something is not quite right, or that something needs to be repositioned or removed. In this living room there may be an old couch of no further use and ready for tossing. Just as in the living body, there are times when certain parts are no longer serviceable and need to be removed.

I had a patient in my office who really needed surgery but did not want it. As we talked, I suggested she might try to consider it more like a gardener pruning a tree. The purpose for cutting off the limbs is not to punish the limbs or to kill them. Instead, removing the part that no longer serves the tree harnesses its energy to grow more vigorously and completely. Pruning focuses and directs the life force to bring more life and health to the tree as a matter of focus and purpose. When my patient understood this, she was able to move forward with the surgery.

Jesus said, "I came to give you life and that more abundantly." It is this abundant life we are seeking in Living Medicine.

Living Medicine includes the reality of pain and sickness, depression, anger, the sense of failure and even death. But it also enhances joy, laughter, hope, love and the breath of life. By awakening all of our senses, we will see more clearly, hear more deeply and feel more surely. The living room is where we allow all of these feelings into our dwelling place.

In order to reach the mountaintop, we must first cross the valleys. If we are afraid to allow ourselves to feel grief and pain, we cannot feel the fullness of joy and happiness.

Happiness does not exist by itself without sorrow, fear or conflict, but by working through the difficult places and finding a way through. These valleys of emotion will enter into our house and we are challenged to entertain them and do something with them.

It is in our living room that we have the opportunity to enjoy music and entertainment according to what we choose. If we choose to listen to a symphony, we must understand that each musician, as an individual, needs to understand the music, instrument and composition that s/he is working with and will spend hours upon hours practicing and perfecting the skill. In a symphony even the musician who plays the triangle has to understand his instrument, the place where his note will be played and the proper way in which to do this. In the overall rendition of the symphony, that note played by the triangle may seem insignificant but, without it, the symphony would not be complete.

When I think of the discipline, the patience and the concentration required for a musician to play that one note, it is truly awesome. The solo of the flute is important but, without the harmony of the rest of the orchestra, it would not have such a powerful impact. In an orchestra, every note played by every musician is important for the overall beauty of the rendition. So it is with the human body. There is no part of our body that can be complete without the cooperation and harmony of the other components. Every molecule of our physical body is in relationship with its other elements. Every story told in the living room becomes part of the very music of this home and creates a living space.

During his training as a resident in ophthalmology, my youngest son, David, an ophthalmologist, had a professor who, when David presented a case describing the patient's life and other aspects of his health, said, "I don't want to hear about any of that. All I want to hear about is the eye." Granted, the eye needs to be studied and understood as a single structure. However, by itself, it is useless to the person.

Everything that happens to me, as a person, is recorded in my physical, mental and spiritual structure. Every thought and every emotion that I experience is as much a part of me as the food I eat. We are a work in process, and we are constantly creating who and what we are. We are even, moment by moment, creating our past. The thoughts that I think, the words that I say, the books that I read, the pictures that I see, the nature that I adore – all of these make up who and what I am. The more I understand the instrument that I am, the more I practice focusing on my ideal so that my thoughts are constructive and healing. As a result, the truer my instrument will be in its presentation of the musical note that I am in this lifetime.

Many living rooms have a fireplace as a focal point and I find its symbolism quite fascinating. I was talking with friends recently about fireplaces and chimneys and was reminiscing about the fireplaces where I grew up in India, as well as the three hearths in the Phoenix home where my children were raised. We only used the one in the living room, and it became a true centerpiece for gatherings. We all enjoyed building the fire, stoking it and keeping it going on winter nights. We watched the flames, talked about the colors and fantasized about what was going on within the fireplace.

Once in a while something would happen – the damper would get stuck, or there would be an obstruction in the chimney so that the airflow would stop, with smoke building up and filling the room. The fire itself would smolder and sometimes die unless we got the airflow moving properly again. In the meantime, we would have suffered from burning eyes, an inability to see well in the room, coughing, irritation of our lungs and just general discomfort.

The fire, as long as it was contained and properly mixed with oxygen, was a joyful, healing, family experience. But, left uncontrolled and obstructed, it became an irritating and even dangerous experience. Occasionally, one of the children would put too much wood or flammable material in the fireplace and we had to wet it down to control it. If we take the symbol of the fire in the fireplace and apply it to ourselves, we can see the importance of the proper control of energy as it moves up from the third chakra where anger, fear, resentment and hate reside, to the fourth chakra, or the love center, where air is the element with a predominance of healing and love.

We know that anger can cause many destructive forces within the entire body, just like fire can, if uncontrolled. However, when the life force, or energy, moves through the fire or the anger up through the chimney, we find that the force of love lifts and transforms the anger into beauty and calmness. Fire is energy; air is energy; and anger is creative energy, as is love. This energy needs to flow so that the fire, or the creative energy at the level of the adrenals, can truly be an active force. If the oxygen does not mix with the fire adequately, the flames smolder and die. In dealing with ourselves and our children, if we keep telling ourselves we must not get angry, we can make that creative energy smolder and die, or build up and become explosive.

Controlled anger remains essential to our growth just as controlled fire is essential to life. Many of our chronic illnesses result from misdirected energy or anger gone blind, which is hate. If misdirected or contained, arthritis, high blood pressure, stomach ulcers, colitis, dermatitis and other conditions can develop. Medications can often control the symptoms but, until the proper flow of energy is reestablished, true healing does not take place. We seem to understand anger when it explodes and causes trouble – just as when a fire burns out of control – but we have trouble understanding the smoldering anger that creates the conditions for the explosion. Anger can be held in our bodies for years before it explodes as in an illness. If we depend completely on medications to control the symptoms, the smoldering fire continues to pose a problem. However, when we allow this energy to flow again through prayer, meditation and the use of the fruits of the spirit, then true healing can take place.

Anger of itself is not bad, and we all have times when it erupts. Even Jesus chased the money-changers out of the temple. Anger itself is a clear emotion, with many ways of expressing it without causing harm to ourselves or anyone else. We can go dig in the garden; we can run or workout; or we can find some humor in the situation. Perhaps we should recognize anger as someone visiting us in our living room and choose how we are going to treat that particular person, whether we will engage them in conversation, ignore them or rebuff them.

Every day we face experiences at our front door that require choices for what we will do with them and how we will relate to them. Most of these decisions are made on an unconscious level while others are reached consciously. Each experience brings with it an emotional response and an actual physical reaction. Those that come to our front door can appear in the form of persons, ideas, activities in the outer world, changes in our environment, or anything else that we might experience day-by-day and moment-by-moment.

As we open the door to these particular experiences, we either allow them to step over the threshold or send them away. If they do step over the threshold, we then have the choice of standing in the foyer and talking to them for a few minutes and then letting them go or inviting them in, perhaps for a cup of tea and a social time together, and then letting them go. We may even invite them in for dinner and then decide to have them stay overnight, sometimes for a day or sometimes for a week, sometimes for months, and sometimes for a lifetime.

If the experience brings the emotion of anger to our front door and we simply address the rage and let it go, we probably will not even remember the situation. If it is appealing enough to invite it in for whatever length of time we chose, then our involvement with it as part of our actual dwelling place becomes stronger. If we allow the anger to enter and stay with us for months and even years, it will bring its relatives of envy, jealousy and self-pity. As these relatives become stronger and invite in other guests, the very essence of our being, our soul, gets pushed farther and farther into the part of the dwelling place that moves us into a mode of survival.

The soul's ideal is tucked away in its office where it continues to do its work and perform its duties. It presents a facade to the outer world that everything is just fine. The soul's ideal even convinces itself that things are adequate, but the person's self-image, self-worth and inner reality will be so overwhelmed by the presence of anger within its dwelling place that the soul hardly recognizes itself. The outer world even labels the individual as "an angry person."

This reminds me of an amaryllis bulb given to me last Christmas that bloomed and graced my home. Then the flower wilted, with the leaves drying up and the bulb shrinking down until it looked totally dead. Thinking there was no life left, I put it out in my garden and forgot about it. I imagine that the bulb felt useless, abandoned and unloved. With a life not worth living, it felt dead. However, it landed in a part of my garden where the soil was rich with life. A rain shower came along and then sun came out, and within itself it began to feel a stirring, an awakening, and it knew it was not dead. Within its very being there was still the ideal, the life and the part that could be and should be revived. It knew that it had to find the life force within its roots to penetrate the earth, move the ground apart, and then to begin to build itself back up again and create a new dwelling place – as it is doing right now.

When we choose a profession, it comes to our front door as a welcome guest. But, if we take it in and allow it to take over our whole life so that the very essence of our being is squeezed into a small corner, we may lose our real self. Sometimes we can awaken to our real self and say we are going to move the professional obsession, or whatever the issue was, out and reclaim our dwelling place. Or there are times when we literally are so shrunken within ourselves that we are tossed out and have to, out of necessity, re-create an entirely new dwelling place. This can be more beautiful, more serviceable and more in tune with the world around us and our own nature than the older dwelling place ever was.

This is true for many of us who have, like Esau in the Bible, sold our birthright for a mess of pottage. The beautiful thing is that it is never too late to reclaim our birthright. Once we recognize our situation, we can always come alive and with God's help rebuild.

This also reflects what has happened in the field of medicine. The true spirit of healing and the art of healing have been so neglected and misunderstood that it requires a new structure. With the tremendous advances the science of medicine has made, we need to allow the advances to remain in their proper place and perform the work that they need to do. We must not let science take over and displace the real heart and soul of the work of healing, which we call the practice of medicine.

One of the fruits of the spirit so vital in removing the blocks to our energy flow is forgiveness – forgiveness of ourselves and of others. The central part of the Lord's Prayer states: "Forgive us our debts as we forgive our debtors." It then goes on to say: "Deliver us from evil." Perhaps evil could be viewed, in this context, as illness.

The second definition of evil in the dictionary is "harmful or injurious," and the third is "accompanied by misfortune or suffering." Used in these contexts, illness becomes something that we would like to be delivered from. Illness often leads to death, and the word *evil* spelled backwards spells *live.* Whether we actually overcome an illness or learn to live with it, we are asking in this prayer for divine help in addressing it.

Laughter offers another way of moving our energy. Linus Pauling scientifically demonstrated this through his work in the mid-sixties. Edgar Cayce said that Jesus was even able to joke on the way to his crucifixion and able to keep the energy flow going through the most awfully painful situation. Then, perhaps, using him as an example, we can truly tap into the real healing energy. As we are healed, so is the world around us.

Our living room offers a place where we often feel strong emotions. These can resemble fearsome storms but, when they clear, we find new hope, clearer air and an opportunity to rebuild. Strong emotions can represent these storms. If we give ourselves the chance to experience them and then take time to rebuild from them, things become significantly better and we feel stronger.

Our living room can provide a safe place to heal pain, whether it is physical, mental or spiritual in nature. There is healing energy in pain.

Physical pain gives a signal, informing us of where we might have a problem that needs addressing. It is felt at the physical level unless it is interrupted by nerve damage, or we are anesthetized, asleep or under the influence of hypnosis. While physical pain itself does not always suggest a problem, it needs to be felt.

Mental pain also needs to be felt. If we do not allow ourselves to experience mental and emotional pain, we may move into senility, Alzheimer's or other forms of psychosis, or simply may not be sensitive to what is happening in our lives.

Then, on the level of spiritual pain, if we try to avoid it, we shut ourselves off from other people and the world and God, and we really die within ourselves. If we really allow ourselves to feel pain on all levels – without getting stuck in it but recognizing it and trying to understand the reason for its presence and its message – we are then able to alleviate it and, at a depth level, live abundantly.

Another emotion we will encounter in this living room of Living Medicine is fear. Fear needs to be recognized for what it is and dealt with. I had a patient call me because she was scheduled to receive a blood transfusion. She was afraid to do this due to concern about AIDS and hepatitis. She had undergone chemotherapy for lung cancer, so her blood count had dropped dangerously low and required a blood transfusion. It seemed a little strange that she was afraid of AIDS and hepatitis when the illness she was struggling with was already so devastating. However, her fear was present and very real to her, so I had no reason to question her feelings.

I explained that there were millions of people who had transfusions without contracting an infection. In addition, the current rigorous checks and safeguards ensured that the chances of contracting AIDS or hepatitis from a blood transfusion remained very, very slim. This did not alleviate her fear.

Then we discussed the possibility of her looking at it in a different way. Perhaps she could realize that, somewhere in this world, there was a person who loved and cared for her enough to give her their very life's blood so she could live. This individual did not know who she was, and she had no knowledge about the person either. This represents true unconditional love from one heart to the other. One has to give and the other has to receive. Who knows; perhaps the healing and love in the blood offered exactly what she needed in order for the chemotherapy to become effective.

If she accepted it as a gift of love, hope and faith, without fear and doubt, it could present the miracle she was looking for. Just to visualize those loving red cells going through her body, touching all of her cells with love and healing and bringing the physical gift of oxygen to all parts of her body, would be a creative thing to do. With this in mind, she was able to go ahead and get the transfusion, with the life-giving aspect of Living Medicine becoming a reality.

Another guest we will find in our living room is grief and her close cousin, depression. Currently, Mother Earth is expressing her grief by the tsunami, the hurricanes, the earthquakes, the floods and the landslides that have been manifesting all around the world. We have not listened to what she has been trying to tell us. We are bleeding her to death by removing oil from the very heart of her being. This oil represents her life blood and cannot be replaced. We have no transfusion to offer her. In our ignorance, we're doing to her what our ancestors did to George Washington: To help him heal, they told him he needed a blood-letting which, of course, is what killed him.

Mother Nature bestows us with many sources of energy. We have solar energy, hydrogen energy, wind energy, and energy from the water – resources available to us that are sustainable and constantly replacing themselves. I wonder when we are going to invite Mother Nature into our living room and say, "We love you; we want to work with you; and we want to keep and support you in any way that we can." She has been so hospitable to us yet we have been so rude to her. She has welcomed us at every level and accommodated us as best she could, and we have not only ignored her but brutalized her.

We are so afraid of what Mother Nature can do that we close our doors to her and try to keep her out while, at the same time, we attack her at every chance we get in order to further our own wishes and wants. Knowing that Mother Nature is in such deep pain, I like to visualize taking her in my arms, sitting in a rocking chair, and rocking her like I would one of my children or grandchildren.

When I celebrated my seventy-fifth birthday with my daughter and her two sons, Daniel, the older boy, said to me, "Nanny, how old are you?" I said, "Daniel, I'm seventy-five years old." He said, "Is that old?" I replied, "Some people think it's old, but don't try to wipe the wrinkles off my face. They belong there and I deserve every one." He then said to me, "When you get to be really, really old and you are really, really sick, I'm going to pick you up in my arms and take you up to your room and rock you, and rock you, and rock you." To me that was the nicest birthday present he could have given me. I know that he had a little book that talked about this, but the important thing is that he remembered it.

Now, if we could just transpose that to Mother Earth who is really, really old and is really, really sick, and rock her and rock her and rock her, how much healing could come about. How much loving could be manifested, and how truly grateful she would be! She is certainly a welcome guest in my living room.

During the Gulf War, I had patients who came to see me for depression. There were so many of them complaining about depression that I began to look at it and wonder: Why now? Why were people going through depression then and more than they had several months before? I began asking people when this depression started and what it was like. Then we looked deeper at what they were dealing with. The thing that emerged was that they were all grieving – for a son or a relative who was overseas, for the people in the Middle East who were suffering; and for Mother Earth whose oil fields were being burned. Most importantly, they were grieving for themselves – and it was a deep, soul-level grief. We realized it was not depression and that there is a difference between grief and depression. After the shock of 9/11 and the fear associated with it, this phenomenon occurred again. Currently, we are still at war, and grief still poses a serious problem.

I looked up grief and depression in the dictionary and found that these words aren't even synonyms. The ones for *grief* include: *suffering, sorrow, regret, disappointment* and *distress*. The synonyms for *depression* are *rejection, gloom* and *downcast*. Even in the dictionary, these two are not considered the same and yet, in our culture, we deal with them as identical issues.

As I began working with people who learned to express and address their grief, the whole feeling of sadness shifted. They realized they were not depressed but grieving. Grief is an emotion; it is something that we all share. There are times of grief in everybody's life and that emotion is completely personal and individual. What one person grieves over would not be something that another person would find sad.

I have patients grieving over a cat that died, or a plant or a job that had been lost, or a remark that someone made that caused them to lose their self-respect or relationship with that particular person. Grief is an ongoing emotional process that we all deal with in our own way, day-by-day. As we recognize our grief and work through it, allowing ourselves to grieve, we grow. If we try to suppress it or bypass it, grief becomes a deep-seated problem that can actually become a physical symptom. Grief is natural and needs to be expressed. It helps to share grief with other people and not dwell on it too much while allowing it to manifest as it will. Grief cannot be medicated; it has to be experienced.

I have a friend whose husband of thirty-eight years died and she, of course, was grieving very deeply. After two years she came into the office one day saying she didn't know what was wrong with her because she was still grieving her loss and people said it was about time she got over it. My response was that we do not have the right to tell another person when the grief process is complete. How long it takes, the form it takes, and how it is dealt with are completely individual processes and part of the growth of that particular soul. We just need to support each other through it.

Depression, on the other hand, can be medicated and frequently should be medicated. Depression is a pathological process that should be identified and dealt with frequently from a medical point of view. But to confuse grief with depression does not allow for the normal process of growth that is part of our lives as human beings.

The scripture passage from John 11:35 speaks of when Jesus was called to the grave of Lazarus, who had been dead for four days: "Jesus wept." In John 11:36, the Jews said, "Behold, how He loved him." Love and grief are very close companions. If we love someone deeply, there will be times when we are going to grieve. If we truly care about the world around us, there are going to be times when we will grieve.

Some of the happiest people I know are those who allow themselves to grieve. Individuals who tap the deep, profound emotion of love and touch their deep core recognize a love that passes all understanding. Then, when something happens in their life that is painful, they can grieve and then go on with their lives.

The deepest grief we have is when we feel separated from our source, or God. Bringing God back into our lives comes about when we recognize the grief and deal with it.

One of the best ways of working with grief is to reach out to someone else who is grieving. As we share our grief and our love, we become stronger and the world becomes stronger. When lonely people retreat into their aloneness, they become engulfed in it. But, if they look around for another lonely person, they find courage to break out of the aloneness.

When we are at war and the people all around us are grieving, Mother Nature is also grieving, and the world is deeply, deeply caught up in grief. At this particular time, it becomes essential that we recognize the grief. We need to reach out and see what we can do to help each other, so the hope and joy and life itself moves and does not remain blocked by unrecognized grief. We can say, "That is so sad," and then move toward helping each other carry our load and working together for a more loving, more compassionate and more considerate world.

One of the universal laws is "Like attracts like." When we choose to have a home, whether it is our body or the actual house where we live, we can manifest our desires, our hopes and our dreams. The key for us is to recognize these hopes, desires and dreams and accept them when they show up at our front door. For some reason, in our culture, we have created the myth that desire is an evil thing. And yet, creativity is derived from desire itself. Put into action with imagination, desire allows us to create and develop new concepts and new blessings.

Somehow, we have condemned desire by associating it with the Garden of Eden story in which Eve saw the fruit and found it desirable. When and why desire became evil from that point on is a mystery to me. Without desire, we would never move out of our stuck places. We really would not grow.

Desire is a great human potential. What we desire then becomes our choice. If we choose beauty, health and joy in our lives, we attract those things into our lives. This does not mean the circumstances that arrive are necessarily beautiful or joyful. Our response to those circumstances that we have attracted results from our desire.

On the other hand, if our desires are constantly negated by thoughts of our own inadequacies, or if we judge or punish ourselves, then the desires that may produce beautiful results are averted or destroyed. For example, if I desire an abundant life that is healthy, I need to accept the aspect that creates health

– diet, exercise, thoughts and relationships – things which bring health into my life. Otherwise my negative thoughts – my anger, jealousy or frustration – attract negativity, which grows and becomes more powerful.

One time, when I went to visit my youngest son in Flagstaff, Arizona, his five-year-old son met me and opened the door without saying a word. He looked me up and down several times. Finally, looking at me straight in the face, he said, "Nanni, you're a good person." To me, that was the most wonderful Christmas gift he could have given me. I came into the family's living room and was accepted not just as their grandmother, but as a "good person." What we accept into our living room remains our choice. Usually, it is an invited guest, but sometimes we have someone whom we did not invite. How we receive that person is our choice.

When we open the door and let someone into our living room, that act impacts our whole life. In this house of Living Medicine, there are certain facts and certain thoughts that come to our front door. We allow them in, we welcome them in, or we close the door and do not allow them to enter.

This was very real some years ago when I was going through an extremely difficult time. There were facts and thoughts that, over a period of years, kept presenting themselves at my front door. At the time, I was neither strong enough nor in an area of consciousness where I could welcome this information in my home. I could not have handled the impact of these facts and thoughts and was in no way ready to deal with what they would have done to my entire life at that time. So I turned them away over a period of years. Finally, different things occurred in my life so that my front door was literally blown open when my husband of 46 years asked for a divorce.

They entered into my living room in such a way that I could not turn them away and I could not get rid of them. My life has not been the same since. In many respects, it has been richer in spite of the fact that all of the furniture in my living room had to be changed or updated.

Somebody once asked me how I was able to manage what was going on in my life during those years. As I thought about it, I pondered how the desert tree roots itself. If it hits a caliche layer, which is comprised of clay so solid that it resembles cement, it has two options. One is to let its roots grow out sidewise without attempting to penetrate the caliche layer, in which case it dies. The other is for it to put all its energy into breaking through that caliche layer until it reaches its source, at which point nothing can knock it over. The winds of time and the storms that hit do not affect it because it remains solidly connected to its source.

I feel that through the years, while dealing with these issues, I was in the process of putting my roots down deeply enough until I reached my source. I focused all my energy on maintaining my home and taking care of my patients. That fit in with my ideal, which was an ideal to serve God with all my heart and mind and soul. I had to let my tap root be in direct contact with my source, or God.

I believe that when my front door was blown open and I was able to go on with my life, I had to redecorate my home. This presented a new opportunity to grow. I could have sat down in my rocking chair and let life pass me by. I am thankful that I was able to feel the excitement of the new situations that enriched my life.

There are so many things in life that come to our front door and which, when we welcome them, make life more wonderful. One of these is the value that healing touch has in the very act of survival.

I recently heard a preacher tell the story of a grandfather whose daughter had a very premature baby girl. Weighing just a little over a pound, she remained in a hospital incubator. Since the infant's father was not in the picture, the nurse asked the grandfather when he went to see his new granddaughter if he would assume the role of her father. This meant coming to see the baby every day, talking to her and telling her that he loved her. As he did so, he was to touch her with his fingertips and massage her little hands and feet and body with his fingertips.

The nurse said, "This baby will connect your voice with your touch, and that is going to mean as much to her as anything that we can do here." The grandfather happily agreed to do this, and the baby thrived.

During World War II, some children in a London orphanage were held and touched, while others were not, despite receiving the same care. The ones who were not touched deteriorated those who were touched thrived.

Years ago I remember seeing a television program called Omni, which focused on touch. It showed a person who was given the job of watching people use a pay telephone. This individual would go up to the person who had been talking on the phone and say, "You know, I really need to make a phone call, but I don't have a dime. Could you lend me one?" (This was when phone calls cost a dime.) The people whose arms he touched when making the request all gave him the dime. If he did not touch their arms, they did not give him the money.

In conventional medicine, many physicians never touch their patients if they do not have a stethoscope. In my experience, many people really hunger for a friendly touch. We get jostled and bumped around in crowds, but to be touched by a person who cares and who is interested in us can be very, very therapeutic. I have found that a hug will frequently not only help to relax a patient but start a healing.

Many people who would really love a hug are afraid to initiate the process. This may be due to fear of rejection and, in part, because they have never initiated personal contact. It's difficult for them to get past their restrictions and shyness, and they feel that initiating a hug would be inappropriate. The comment "To be lovable, one must be 'love-able,'" speaks to the physical touch. In order to be touchable, we have to be "touch-able." To me, this means that if we are hungering for a touch, we should be looking for those people who seem to need a touch and ask them if we can give them a hug.

During one of the live-in programs at our clinic in the mid-1980s, a group of participants gathered for a healing at a soul level. There were fifteen people in the group, and all of them were very self-contained, self-sufficient people who really did not like to be hugged or even participate much in any bodily contact. As we went through the 10-day program, they had dreams and experiences that helped to identify the underlying feelings keeping them separate from each other.

One of the participants was an elegant, sophisticated, self-contained woman in her early forties who felt that she and her twin sister never really wanted to hug or touch each other even as little girls. Several people even made the comment that they had always felt like lepers who should not be touched. By the end of the session, every one of the participants had come to grips with a feeling of having spent a past lifetime as a leper in which they had been ostracized and were not allowed to touch or be touched. As they accepted and understood this, their feelings began to change and, by the end of the session, they experienced no problem with hugging and touching. They even were able to sit at the table close together and hold hands during grace.

I believe that the importance of touch represents one of the reasons people recommend massages. Of course, massage also is important for lymphatic drainage, to stimulate the nerves, to help coordinate the cerebrospinal and the sympathetic nervous systems and to alleviate muscle spasms. On a deeper level, it is vital because we, as human beings, need to touch each other and to be touched by one another in a loving, caring, helpful way.

Inappropriate touching is neither loving nor caring; it is selfish and crude. In a world such as ours, to have the negative aspect of touch eliminate the positive is to let darkness overtake light.

As we get older, it is very important that we give and receive love and caring in the form of touch. In fact, this world needs a program in which small children and the elderly can interact. The little ones need to experience the loving touch and wisdom of a time-worn hand, while the elderly should encounter the smooth, soft touch and pure energy of a toddler. This concept had been a dream of Elisabeth Kübler-Ross, M.D., who was a friend and patient of mine for many years.

Elisabeth loved tea parties. No matter how sick she was, she would offer me a cup of tea in her living room – the place in the home where people first gather for tea parties and discussion groups.

Ever since 1957, I have had a weekly study group in my living room, where we discuss all manner of issues dealing with our spiritual growth. So this area of my home has become a place for spiritual growth and represents my sanctuary and holy place. This is where many tears have been shed and much joy and laughter experienced. It is where my grandchildren come and pull out the pillows and spend the night. It is very much a place of ongoing life and experience.

The way we greet people who come to our front door depends on what is going on in our lives. There are times when a person comes to my front door and says, "I'm so happy to see you. You haven't changed a bit." I may not have seen them for ten years. While this is meant as a compliment and I take it as such, the more I think about that, I am not so sure it is. If ten years have gone by and I have not changed, should I consider that a compliment? Perhaps it reflects that my life has stood still and I have not really learned a lot or experienced the living process at a deeper level. I do not need to look the same as I did when I was sixty or seventy years old. I would hope that some of the things I have experienced would show on my face and person. My experiences can help my children and grandchildren so they can benefit from my changes.

Take my little grandson, Taylor, who is a true teacher for me. We were discussing things of interest to a six-year-old boy one hot Arizona day in my living room when suddenly, out of the clear blue sky, he stopped all conversation. Looking me straight in the eye, he said, "Nanni, I think the meanest thing that anybody could do would be to kill all the teddy bears and the blankies." I thought that was really cute and went on talking about other interesting subjects to him. When I thought about it later, I realized that this was a very profound and insightful statement; it wasn't just cute.

Our children have so much wisdom to share with us, and it is so easy for us to think that our thoughts and deliberations are more important than their insights. To me, the idea of killing the teddy bears and blankies says that we need to be very aware of the nurturing aspect of divine energy and that we cannot live life fully without letting tenderness and compassion enter into our everyday lives. We have done so much harm taking away the arts and nurturing programs from our schoolchildren in our attempt to have them fit into certain proscribed patterns.

I wonder what the children in war-torn Iraq are doing for blankies and teddy bears. No wonder the world is angry. Perhaps we could have a project of dropping blankies and teddy bears instead of bombs. Maybe we cannot give them the material blankies and teddy bears, but we can all pray for them and hold them in our hearts with our loving concern.

But I realize it is not just the little children who need this kind of concern but the child in each one of us is looking for and wanting to share love and compassion.

I know a young person entering medical school who has taken his blankie with him. It is pretty much of a rag by now, but it continues to offer him comfort. I believe that, because of his awareness of his own needs, he will become a truly good doctor.

In the Bible, when Jesus and his disciples were faced with the problem of feeding 5,000 hungry people, it was a small boy who produced the five loaves and two fishes that Jesus blessed and used to feed them all with twelve baskets left over (John 6:1-14). We all need to look for and accept the gifts children bring to us and then bless them and share them with each other. This is the aspect of creative energy that must be made manifest on this dimension.

Shifting our interest and concern from the finer things in life to the power of money and materiality injures our souls.

The use of creative energy has always been important for the nurturing of the human soul.

Mary Poppins' statement, "A spoonful of sugar makes the medicine go down," truly represents a fundamental truth. We all need some sweetness and tenderness in our lives, especially to help us deal with the "medicine" we have to take. We all have some difficult karmic patterns to live with. As we recognize this in ourselves and others, we can look for opportunities to be kind and gentle with the hurt parts of ourselves and others. An attitude of tenderness and softness, which brings laughter and humor into the most difficult situations, can evoke a healing when nothing else can.

For many years physicians saw patients in their living room, particularly in small towns and rural areas. When I practiced medicine in Wellsville, Ohio, there were many times when patients were brought to my front door and examined in my living room, even though I had an office in town. Though inconvenient, it was a reality and had to be dealt with.

I'll never forget one late afternoon when the polio epidemic was rampant in Ohio. I had just returned home and taken my children upstairs for their bath and storytelling time when the phone rang. A frightened caller said that his child was very sick and he didn't know what was wrong. I told him to give me fifteen to twenty minutes to get a babysitter and I would come by to see the child.

However, in less than ten minutes my doorbell rang and, when I went to the door, he came in carrying his six-year-old daughter. He was afraid that she had polio. Since he was already in my living room, I could not send him back out and had to instruct my children to stay at the head of the stairs and not come down. The child did not have polio, and

I was able to alleviate the father's fears and help the child as she began to heal.

Those of us who work as physicians are constantly faced with situations symbolized by the story I have just told. Because we have taken on this role, our living room or our living place is frequently disrupted by people who do not recognize our boundaries. We could be in line at the grocery store or at a party or any place life takes us. If we are recognized in our professional role, people feel free to ask us questions and advice. I know of no formula for dealing with life on these terms.

What it requires is for us to be present and aware of the circumstances enough so that we can set the necessary boundaries, such as making the children stay at the head of the stairs, and deal with the issues as they are presented to us. Life seldom separates work and personal issues in such a way that we can just "deal with things in the office" according to our plan. Because we have chosen the profession of healing, the universe brings to our front door issues that need to be dealt with at that time and place.

I remember another time when the mayor of this small town in Ohio came to my front door with a large laceration on his elbow, bleeding and in pain. I had my medical bag with me, so, with my children running in and out and up and down, I repaired his elbow right there on my kitchen table.

Even now, though I am officially retired and not practicing as a physician, there is no way that I can turn my back on, or turn away from, somebody who is asking for help. The front door of my living room or my consciousness will be open to people as long as I can be of service. It also will be open to new thoughts, new concepts and new experiences as long as I am consciously able to make those decisions.

In this war-torn world of ours, we can truly destroy ourselves – just as iatrogenic medicine (one that causes a problem by clearing another) can complicate the healing process and even make it worse. Perhaps the time has come when we shift our attention from killing people and diseases to the true healing aspects of nurturing and love. I believe Jesus meant it when he said, "Love your enemies." If disease is one's enemy, love could make a difference, and we choose how we deal with the guests in our living room.

Chapter Four

The Kitchen and Dining Room

*I*n our house of Living Medicine, the kitchen and dining room are so open to each other that they almost resemble one unit. The reasons for this become more apparent as we look close at this unit.

Golda Meir, the president of Israel from 1969 to 1974, was a woman of deep insight, with an extraordinary ability to communicate and bridge gaps in the international community that remained unaddressed. She did most of her negotiations and office work in her kitchen and at the dining room table. Here she brought the heads of state from all around the world, offered them a cup of tea and some food, and then began the serious negotiations. In this family setting and sharing of food and drink, many of the hostilities that loomed so great were brought into perspective and dealt with. It is hard to hide things under a table when that table is your kitchen table. There are many acceptable ways for people to hide things from one another in executive offices and corporate rooms. This is very difficult in the open communication that happens around a dining room table.

One of the central rituals in most of the major religions involves breaking bread together. Jesus' last gathering with his disciples is commemorated throughout Christendom as the

Lord's Supper. (Matthew 26:26-30) The place where our hearts open up to each other, where we share laughter and tears, where friends and enemies gather and look at each other face-to-face is across a dining room table.

The Twenty-third Psalm, which is a major scriptural passage for Jews and Christians, reflects the symbolism: "Thou preparest a table before me in the presence of mine enemies." God has prepared this table for us – a place where we can face and communicate with those aspects of our being that are "our enemies." By now, in this house of Living Medicine, we have invited people in who have become part of who and what we are.

Our enemies no longer represent external aspects of ourselves but now become those parts of ourselves we are uncomfortable with and in conflict with. These are our fears and our hopes that may get dashed, our feelings about different people, our past pain and hurts that we carry with us all of the time, our resentments and prejudices. They are also the things we don't like about ourselves: "My feet are too big;" "My nose is too large;" "I'm too fat;" and "I'm too thin." Whatever it is that we see within ourselves that we do not like becomes our enemy.

These enemies cause disease processes in our body. Our fears can manifest as stomach ulcers or colitis. Our anger and resentments can send our blood pressure up. Our jealousy often causes heart problems, and so the list goes on. The Twenty-third Psalm says, "Thou preparest a table before me in the presence of mine enemies." It is not that there is a tablecloth that is being spread over this so we don't have to look at them. The fact is, that at this place, at this time and in this area of our being, we are looking at and are confronted with either making friends with our enemies or trying to suppress them and continue the process of maintaining animosity.

Webster's dictionary defines *enemy* as: *1. A person who feels hatred for or fosters harmful designs against another; an adversary or opponent. 2. An armed foe; an opposing military force. 3. Something harmful or prejudicial.* So, rather than internalizing the enemy aspects of ourselves, it becomes critical that we deal with our enemies in an open and clear way, just as Golda Meir did.

As we open ourselves to receiving, the dining room/ kitchen area is where nutrition and nourishment on all levels of our being takes place – body, mind, and spirit. The substances with which we feed these create who and what we are.

One of the things we have learned and know about the food we eat is that certain foods increase the good and bad cholesterol in our bloodstream and that other foods help keep it down. We have not really learned how much emotion and attitudes affect what we eat and how we eat, but this is something that we are becoming more informed about every day. Cholesterol has become a big scary word and people who know little about their own physiology are aware of the effect that it has on their bloodstream.

I have a seventy-six year old patient who was in my office as a follow-up to a physical exam. As I gave her the results, I mentioned that her cholesterol was elevated. I did not go into a great deal of discussion about what she should do to lower it since it was not very high. However, she decided to take care of this problem on her own. Realizing that if she stopped eating two things that she dearly loved and ate – bacon and peanut butter – she probably could bring her cholesterol down. Being a very wise woman, she came up with a constructive way to deal with the problem.

She went with her husband and her daughter to a fancy restaurant, took a candle along with her and sat down at the table. While her husband and daughter ordered their meal, she ordered four strips of crisp bacon. While her family was eating, she talked to the bacon and said something like, "Bacon, I've always loved you; you've been very good to me. We've had a long and constructive relationship, but now is the time for us to part. I am going to leave you with a great deal of love and fondness and happy memories. I will eat two pieces and leave the remaining two on my plate so I know that you are always here for me if I need you." After talking for a little while longer to bacon, she blew out the candle, and they paid their bill and left.

She has not wanted bacon since that time. I asked, "What did you do about the peanut butter?" She said, "Oh, that was fun. I got a new jar of peanut butter, put it on a little silver tray, and walked through my home to every place I had eaten peanut butter. I sang something like this: 'Peanut butter, I love you; you've been so good to me. I have many happy memories with you, and now is the time for us to part." When she was finished, she gave the jar of peanut butter to a little girl across the street. She has not wanted peanut butter since.

When I recently asked her about bacon and peanut butter she said, "Oh, yeah, I haven't eaten any." The beauty of it is that her cholesterol is now normal.

What's wonderful about this story is that this wise woman was able to create a delightful ritual that allowed her, with love and caring, to let go of something for which she no longer had any use. She didn't say, "Oh my, I have to stop eating peanut butter and bacon; I don't know how I'm going to do it because they are so much a part of my life." In that case, she would have created a large negative thought form out of the problem and, unable to stop, would have made it her enemy.

Instead, she joyfully brought the whole problem out in the open and took care of it.

As we go through life, we are continually faced with opportunities and challenges to release old habits and patterns. These habits represent emotional and physical thought patterns as well as spiritual mile-markers or for those who think in these terms "karmic trends." This can pose a very painful process and one of the most difficult things we have to face because it involves attachments at all levels of our being.

If we take the approach of "Just say no," it's almost impossible to accomplish the act of letting go. The attachments are too deep and probably very long-standing. Perhaps we can move forward without condemning ourselves if we accept ourselves at our current level of development and recognize we have developed these attachments so we can learn and grow from them. With gratitude for what is and what has been and by creating a personal ritual, we can mitigate that which needs to be released in a painless and even fun manner. It is only when we cling to things, whether material things or even personal relationships, that they continue to have power over us.

With any attachment or addiction, when we come to a place where we must let go, we can choose the path of karma or the path of grace. If we choose karma, it becomes very painful and frequently has physical repercussions. If we choose the path of grace and allow the addiction to move out of our lives with God's help, we create a new pattern that leads us to a fuller life. A ritual involving prayer and meditation, as well as people or friends who help us on the spiritual path, can truly relieve us of lifetimes of attachments.

I have a friend who shared a dream with me and about the financial difficulties she was experiencing in her life. In this dream she was ankle-deep in mud, struggling up a hillside to reach a swimming hole at the top. There were two small wooden carts like the little red wagons some of us had as children. She was pushing one and pulling the other. Two of her friends accompanied her but they were skipping along and dancing and having a great time as they went up this hill. She became very frustrated with the whole process and, in a passive/aggressive way, began saying things like, "I wish somebody would help me carry this load. I wish somebody would realize how hard it is for me to push this wagon which keeps going one way or another and pull the other one up this hill. I wish somebody would really pay attention to the hardships that I am facing."

When she looked in the wagons, they were empty. She stopped in the dream and said, "Time for an attitude change." She let go of the wagon she was pulling and jumped over the wagon she was pushing, stretching out her arms and running up the hill. Her friends had already let go of their load. They were not pushing and pulling empty wagons up the hill through the mud but had released them. Yet she was hanging on to whatever this was that was bogging her down and making it almost impossible for her to get up to the top of the hill.

She said to me, "I realize that I've been feeling like nobody's here to help me. I have to carry this financial load by myself and I've just been having a really hard time doing this and feel all alone. I realize that I am pulling an empty load. I no longer need anything that is in that empty wagon. If I let them go, they will just disintegrate and I can go on. I have no need to keep pulling this load of what probably represents self-pity, anger and resentment up the mountain. That is miserable. It feels horrible. If I let it go, I can get up the mountain and get into that swimming hole, which is where I'm headed."

We cannot really nourish ourselves until we let go of that which we no longer have use for. We cannot add to a cup that is already full. If we want to grow and be nourished, we need to let go.

Although nutrition and diet pose a concern when we talk about our kitchen, the central theme of this book is not about that. Something, however, needs to be said about the importance of these physical aspects. One basic tenet is that the more we can stay with foods that are either minimally processed or not processed at all, the better our nutrition will be.

We recognize that our physical body functions better with natural or live foods, rather than those undergoing multiple procedures that kill their very life essence. This, of course, includes preservatives, excess sugar and salt, food colorings and any of the multitude of processes that alter the state of the food from its natural state. I am certainly not suggesting these be totally eliminated from our diets, but that when we choose our foods, we become aware of how close they are to the natural, or living, state in which they were produced. The whole question of genetic altering is something that we are going to face and deal with at some time since much of our food worldwide has been altered.

Some of the people I know deal with their dietary restrictions in a fanatical way. Afraid to put different types of food into their bodies, they create a state of fear, which shuts down digestive juices and can actually cause more problems than partaking of the food available to them, blessing it, and being grateful for it. It is not just the food we ingest that is important, but the way in which we receive the food, the way in which we ask our body to deal with this food and the total body, mind and spirit connection we work with in the dining room.

It is interesting that the priesthood is purported to have the greatest longevity of any other profession. The Ministers, rabbis and priests all have diets that probably are not the best since they are served foods by parishioners and people who may or may not be concerned with the nutritional value of their offerings. They do, however, always bless their food. They are grateful for what they have, and their body accepts the blessed food with an attitude of gratitude instead of fear.

Years ago Olga Warell, a well-known psychic and healer, did a research project in which she placed her hands around a beaker of water and said a prayer. Subsequent tests found that its molecular structure was changed by her prayer.

The progress of the scientific work with water has been brought to our awareness in great detail by Masaru Emoto, M.D. His books, *The Hidden Message in Water, The True Power of Water*, and *The Secret Life of Water*, explore in depth his theories of how water reflects at its very crystalline level the world around it – even the thoughts and words of people around it. In the movie, *What the Bleep Do We Know?*, he shows magnificent pictures of crystals formed when water is exposed to various words and different types of music.

Since, as human beings, we are mostly made up of water, it is so important that we understand the power of our words in relationship to ourselves and to each other. A kind word creates beautiful crystalline structures within the water of our body whereas cruel words cause disturbance and confusion, resulting in pain or illness. When Jesus spoke of living water, I believe he was referring to a physical reality in relationship to thoughts and words of love and truth. He, as the Great Physician, was able to bring healing and life to the very molecules in our bodies.

This helps us as physicians to understand that, when we talk to patients, the very words we use bring either healing or more problems to them and to ourselves. Our house of Living Medicine, both inside and outside, must be a manifestation of living water.

It is also known that if people eat while they are frightened or angry, it affects the digestive juices within the gut. One of the problems we face in this world of corporate structure is that many meetings are conducted at lunchtime, causing a person to approach the meal with tension and fear, or at least in a state of stress. This causes enough restriction of the digestive process that many medications are prescribed in order to help people to digest their food better and ease their symptoms. I often wonder how many of the current medications could be eliminated if we approached our meals with a blessing and added laughter and love to the table.

It is in the kitchen and the dining room where many of the choices we make in life are manifested. The food we choose, the way we choose to prepare it and the time and place where the food is served all affect our lives and our well-being. When we overeat or do not eat enough, it is a matter of choice.

I had a patient who was so upset with her daughter-in-law because she doesn't peel potatoes properly, leaving some of the eyes on them. Her idea of how her daughter should peel has caused a rift in the family. The matter of the relationship between will and choice becomes vital in this area of the household.

Many years ago during one of the symposia our clinic held, I heard Mark Thurston, Ph.D., describe the concept of the will, and I have never forgotten it. He likened our movement in consciousness to a sailing vessel, with the rudder of the ship representing the will. The rudder keeps the ship on track and allows it to get to its destination. Constructed of strong enough material, it is not easily bent or destroyed by heavy seas and storms in life. The rudder is controlled by the person guiding the ship, and that person is manifests choice.

The difference between choice, which is associated with the second spiritual center or the Leydig cells, and the will, which is manifested in the thyroid, is a matter of structure and function. By our ability to choose, we direct the way the will allows us to follow our chosen path we have chosen.

If our goal is oneness and returning to our original state of oneness with the creator, then it is through the proper use of choice that we direct the will. It must be strong enough to respond to the choice that we make. This hinges on cooperation between our individual choices and the way they direct our will. It is only as we create cooperative action between our physical, mental and spiritual bodies that we truly manifest a balance in our lives, and it is this balance that allows us to be whole. We cannot really manifest God's will in this dimension without having the physical aspect of will functioning harmoniously and in balance.

Cooperation involves much more than just working in tandem with the body itself. It also involves the everyday choices of partnering with other individuals and cooperating with the Earth and the entire universe. The attitude of the person preparing the food has a direct affect on the food. If it is prepared in anger, the food takes on this energy.

During a conference in Council Grove, Kansas, in 2006, Mietek Wirkus and his wife Margaret presented a workshop describing the research they did at the National Institute of Health. A healer and energy worker, Mietek conducted the study while he was in Poland and has been continuing it since he has been in the United States. His work includes energy research for the purpose of healing people.

He has been asked by the National Institute of Health to research cells and cellular structure and the way individual cells absorb their nutrients, specifically in relationship to how they absorb calcium. What the studies demonstrated was that, after cells were exposed to Mietek's healing energy, they absorbed twenty-two percent more calcium than prior to the exposure. The fact that Mietek demonstrated he could increase the uptake of calcium in cells with the use of healing thoughts and healing intention is important. He did this consistently and repeatedly.

Since we know this is possible, we must keep in mind that we truly can increase the calcium absorbed by our bone cells to make stronger bones with our intention and our thoughts. Telling women to fight osteoporosis as though they are going to fight their own bones may be causing more difficulty in our skeletal structure than we have known. Understanding that thoughts are things and that there is reality to what the cells in our body know to do is truly what Living Medicine is about.

One day I went to see a friend at a hospital rehab center. She had been in an automobile accident two months prior and had so severely injured her spine that she was lying in a full-body cast with her head and neck immobilized. She was unable to move any part of her body except her eyes and mouth and could not allow her spine to shift and move so healing could take place. All she could do was lie flat and look at the ceiling.

First she was fed through tubes but then was able to ingest liquids and semi-solid foods through a straw. She had friends bring soups and healthy foods to her in the hospital. Told that her chances of recovering to the point of even being able to sit up were remote, she prepared herself for a life of almost total disability.

I explained to her the role that the osteoblasts and osteoclasts play in bone regeneration – that one of the cells was created to remove debris while the other was designed to rebuild bone tissue. Here's how she describes what happened next:

Dr. Gladys McGarey came to visit. She told me to talk to my cells – they would know what to do. I could not remember exactly what she said when she visited me, but I do know that I had to talk to myself. I told my cells to fix what needed to be fixed. I think, when my body was repairing itself, I must have been on automatic pilot. The fractures at the lower part of my spine were healing while I was lying flat on my back for four months immobile [sic].

She finally was able to begin to move her head a little. She began to sit up, and when they were able to perform X-rays, they found that the spinal column was beginning to heal. She was able to go home after four months and, six months later, she said, "I am home. I can walk. I even opened a jar. My fingers are working better. I walk in the pool every day. The last X-ray showed that my neck is healing. I even now have a normal curve in the curvy part of my neck, which was flat. The doctor feels I will soon be wearing a soft collar, and soon I will even be able to turn my head." What this woman was able to do with her attitude, her mind and her nutrition was to repair damage that the medical community told her was impossible.

I had dinner with her six months after her accident. She sat in a restaurant and drove her own car. The day before she had hiked down to Montezuma's Well and back out again with a friend. She wore a soft collar support decorated with a beautiful necklace. She removed the collar during the dinner, demonstrating that she could hold her head up straight without support for short periods of time. Her friend had performed some energy work and craniosacral adjustments on her, easing the discomfort that had been so severe in her scalp that even the slightest movement of air caused sharp pain. While she still works with restrictions in movement, these, too, are improving.

When I talked to her further about her stay in the hospital and the time when she was unable to do anything but visualize mental pictures, she told me a remarkable story. The devastation her body had suffered was as severe as Katrina had been to New Orleans. She said that when she moved her eyes to the right, she saw it being completely rebuilt. She kept focusing on this city that had been so horribly devastated and recreated it in her mind, street by street, house by house. She even saw the color of the houses and the way the city was being rebuilt. Through her visualization her body began to understand that it, too, could rebuild. She saw the rebuilding of New Orleans as symbolic of the rebuilding of her body, cell by cell and structure by structure.

As she moved her eyes to the other side, she saw an ancient city with a stream running through it with buildings that lined its bank. She saw the color of the buildings, as well as their structure and stability. She did not know where this city was but knew it existed.

About three months later when she was home and watching the Discovery Channel, she saw a picture of Bern, Switzerland, and recognized it as the city she had seen in her visualization. In her mind this picture was a symbol of the underlying pattern of her healing. She recognized the stability and beauty of this city and incorporated that into the rebuilding of her body.

Virginia Veach is a psycho oncologist and psychotherapist who has traveled the world delivering comfort and healing to thousands of people in difficult circumstances. During the Vietnam War, she went to a camp, along with a group of fourteen other people, where they brought hope and healing to severely neglected people who had very little to eat and nothing in the way of support. After her team spent time with them and shared what they could, the people in the camp wanted to do something to let Virginia and her group know how much they appreciated their help. So they prepared a meal for them. They asked the people in the camp to each put one grain of rice in the common bowl. In this manner, they collected enough to create a sparse meal – but a meal, nonetheless.

Since water also remained very scarce, the villagers had one bucketful in which they washed their hands and the dishes, serving that same water to all of the people in her group to drink. Since this was offered to them with love, they put aside any fears about bacterial contamination or illness that might result from drinking such contaminated water. As a result, not one of the fourteen people experienced any symptoms or any illness. When I heard her tell that story, I could not help but glory in the wonderful power that was manifested through love and gratitude.

If a person lives by herself and does not have family or friends to share the dining experience with, it becomes important that she create an environment of health and happiness as she fixes her meals and eats them. This may require imagination and thoughtfulness in order to set the proper table. She can become aware that her friends can be her memories and her thoughts. It is up to her to create the setting of the table and the environment in which she eats.

The kitchen – whether it has chrome-plated fixtures, an electric stove, a refrigerator with an ice maker, running water or an open fire over which the food is cooked – is vital to the way in which that food is prepared and presented. Although I have a fully functioning electric kitchen at this point, I remember as a child having the food prepared over an open fire with no running water available. Instead, our water had to be boiled and stored in containers for drinking. Some of the best meals I ever had were prepared in that manner. Since there was no refrigeration in the jungles where we lived, the food had to be consumed immediately.

In life, we need to learn to meet the needs of the condition. Whatever condition we find ourselves working with at the time, we must adapt and work with it or we become angry and frustrated. When this happens and negative thoughts creep in, our food may not be contaminated with bacteria but it can be, and often is, contaminated by attitude. Food that is prepared by an angry person carries with it the vibrations of that emotion and cannot be as healthy as food prepared by someone with a loving, joyful attitude.

I have friends who are so obsessed with keeping bacterial contamination out of their food that they use chemicals almost constantly to keep the surfaces bacteria free. In the process of doing this, I wonder how much the food is contaminated by chemicals that are used to kill the bacteria itself. I wonder whether the attitude of people who are so intent on destroying life forms, such as bacteria, may be unhealthy not only for them but also for the people who eat the food they prepare.

The food that goes into our bodies should be clean but not sterile. Our kitchens should be clean, but they do not need to be sterile. The conditions in the outdoor kitchen where I grew up were certainly not sterile, and yet we were healthy.

I remember times as a child in the jungles of India when we would come across *dakh* bungalows that served as outposts for the British soldiers. These buildings sat in a remote part of the jungle where the officers would be stationed and frequently not see any Caucasian people for months on end. However, it was part of their discipline, as well as part of just maintaining their sanity and sense of direction, that every night they dressed for dinner and ate at exactly the same time, exercising great care about their manners.

When we lived in the jungles of India, we were much freer and more relaxed about our dining etiquette. Not that we were allowed to be careless and sloppy, but there were times when laughter and storytelling would completely take over and we would be caught up in the life of the situation more than actual properness of table manners. When we would return to town, my mother would say to us, "Now just remember, you're not in the jungle anymore." We would have to try and tame our wild spirits.

In this house of Living Medicine, we need to be aware of what our life is – what is important in our lives and what will increase the living spirit within us – so that the life we live is an abundant one and we adapt to our circumstances. What we choose to eat physically, feed our minds and nurture our spirit with is truly what keeps us alive.

As my children were growing up, we would always gather around the dining room table. There were many times, since my husband and I were both physicians, when our discussion would deal with some specific medical problem or issue. Perhaps that's one of the reasons all six of my children moved into healing professions. The food that they ate was "contaminated" by thoughts and ideas associated with the field of medicine. This is not a bad thing; it was just the way life was. The children brought their lives to the table, including their friends, and we brought ours. As we shared our life experiences, we understood each other better.

One thing I insisted on, no matter what else was going on during the day, was that at six o'clock at night we gathered around the dining room table for dinner. Many were the times when I was called away because of deliveries, or Bill was called away because a patient needed care. Many were the times when something was said at the table that hurt the feelings of one of the girls and she left the table crying. But the times that we really remember were those when we laughed so hard we could hardly sit up, or when the puns that were created were a challenge for all.

As physicians, when we take our patients' history and find out what their diet is like (which is very important and frequently overlooked), we can help them understand the importance of sharing the very experiences of life in an open and healthy way. I know no better place or healthier situation than a dining room table where one person dines with her memories as her table companions – or a family of ten people gathered around the table sharing their joys, their sorrows and their very life experiences in an open and caring way. This ritual can bring life and health and, we, as physicians, are in a position to encourage this type of behavior. The physician within recognizes the importance of shared experiences.

Chapter Five

The Library

In my home, my library sits adjacent to my dining room. It is so full of books that they are stacked on all of the shelves and on the floor. It seems to me that these books keep reproducing themselves. I give books away and more books appear. Many of the books are precious to me, with some being personally autographed. Others are precious because I have read them many times and they have a special message and meaning for me. Still others are precious because they are old and some that belonged to my parents. They are treasures because of their antiquity.

Then there are the many books that I have not read, but they are precious to me because they are in my library – they are in my life, and I know they are there. These books carry philosophy, music, humor, hope, fear, excitement and passion. So many of the emotions and experiences that we humans have are depicted and written about in these books. You might say that my library is my own personal history. It is so updated that I even have my computer in it, as well as my parents' medical diplomas hanging on the wall along with a picture of Kübler-Ross with Mother Teresa. My awards, my diplomas and my family pictures hang on these walls.

Although small, there is so much history packed into this room that it really serves as the central part of my home. The futon pulls out to create a guest room, so life isn't just on what has happened in the past in my library; it is about what is going on right now in my home. It is my present, my future and a record of my past. It is where we buried the time capsule when I built this house. This is the place where I do my writing. It is where I can call up old memories like some of my old books that may not have been visited for years or which are new and fresh.

Having been born and raised in India just on the other side of the Himalayas, I always wanted to see Mt. Everest and never really had the opportunity. So, in 1990, when my brother, Carl Taylor, M.D., invited me to accompany a group of physicians doing some work with the village people in Tibet, I was thrilled. The Chinese and Tibetan governments had asked him to bring a team back into the villages to identify the health problems of the local inhabitants. We went to a village that was at 14,000 feet in elevation and a little farther away from Mt. Everest than we had hoped. But still, Everest should have been in plain sight.

However, since it was July and also the rainy season, clouds covered the mountains the whole time we were there. As we prepared to leave, I thought, "Well, I just will have to come back because I'm not going to get to see Everest this time."

Then, as we were driving back on the bus, for some reason a voice inside me said, "Turn around." I did so and, for a short period of time, the clouds separated and there it was. I yelled, "There's Everest!" and the bus driver slammed on the brakes. But, by the time we got out to take a better look, the clouds had closed over again. We had seen Mt. Everest! For me, it was like a transcendental experience because no one can ever tell me that I have not seen Mt. Everest. In my heart I know it is there, and I know that I had that experience and it was unusually deep and meaningful.

When I got back home, I wondered why this was so important to me. Then I happened to pick up the little book that my father had written. In it was one small chapter just one page long, which began with the statement: "When our trio was to become a quartet..." which meant that my parents already had three children and I, the fourth, was on my way. Dad writes that he and Mom took a trip by horseback up to Simla in the Himalayas and, during this trip, they wanted to get a glimpse of Mt. Everest but, because of the clouds, were unable to see it. I then realized what this was all about. Even in utero I was trying to get a glimpse of Mt. Everest and had not been able to. But now I had finally seen it.

We store memories from this lifetime and past lifetimes in our consciousness that, when needed, can be accessed and made available to us. My father's book with the little story about Mt. Everest brought the experience of my intrauterine life into perspective with my trip in 1990, and this will always be part of my personal history.

One of the exciting treasure hunts in my library has been to find evidence of the evolving timeline in the field of medicine. As I was going through some old papers, I came across an editorial printed in the *Journal of the American Medical Association* on September 5, 1986 quoting one of its prior editorials from September 4, 1886, entitled "The Higher Education of Women." It states:

> *A good professional education is very expensive...not alone...of money, but...of physi-*

ological force; much more than a woman can afford, if she is to perform her proper functions as a producer of men.... The production of children calls for far more physiological force on the part of the mother.... The functions of gestation and maternity require a great outlay of physiological force, and if this force is used up in other work the offspring of the world must suffer, as must the woman herself.

While it may be true that too much bodily labor may render a person less prolific, it is very much more clearly shown that excessive mental labor is a cause of sterility... In its full sense, the reproductive power means the power to bear a well-developed infant, and to supply that infant with the natural food for the natural period. Most of the flat-chested girls who survive their high-pressure education are unable to do this... Our education, our civilization, is one that stunts, deforms and enfeebles women... Shall we make it worse by placing women in competition with men, by still further stunting, deforming and enfeebling her animal powers?

The exciting aspect of all of this comes into focus when we look at the way medicine was practiced 100 years ago and what has happened since then. Women are no longer considered baby machines, although many happily accept that part of our function. Now, in medical schools more than half of the students are women.

The changing face of medicine is bringing the feminine energy back into the practice of medicine. Ancient traditional medicine has always known that true healing must be accompanied by nurturing, support and encouragement, and I believe this is best exemplified by the feminine. When medicine assumed the role of fighting diseases that attack from the outside, it became something that required masculine energy as well as the instrument through which we destroy disease. If all of our energy is directed toward destruction, we will never win this battle.

The feminine energy allows us to rebuild, reconstruct and reactivate the spiritual essence of who we are. It becomes apparent that we need to emphasize and reawaken the gentle, compassionate, healing energy that is manifested in the true feminine and is called love.

Focusing on the relationship of body, mind and spirit is what Living Medicine is all about. The part that women have in initiating this is something we now recognize. True healing needs to embrace a balance of the male and female. Without the nurturing of the feminine, we would continue to fight disease and not have the movement of the spirit as part of the healing process.

I have heard it said, "Women are taught to shrink to fit." It's encouraging that we can now laugh at the concepts held 100 years ago and see that we really have made progress in the way we approach healing of the body, mind and spirit.

When my sister visited me, we went with my daughter, Helene, to the cemetery where my mother and father are buried. When she saw the memorial plate at their grave, Helene was incensed and said, "Mom, how could you do that?" I did not know what she was talking about until I looked again and realized what I had put on the memorial plate. It read: "Dr. John C. Taylor" with "Elizabeth S. Taylor" underneath. No "Doctor," no M.D. title, and no acknowledgement of the fact that she, too, was a doctor. We realized that things had changed through the three generations.

When Mother and Dad were introduced in a group, it would go something like, "This is Dr. John Taylor and his wife, Elizabeth, who is also a doctor." When I was introduced with my husband, both of us being physicians, the person making the introductions would ask me, "Do you want to be introduced as Dr. Gladys McGarey or Mrs. Bill McGarey?" I would say, "It doesn't make any difference, both are all right." The issue was not important.

However, in the third generation when my daughter, Helene, was introduced with her husband also being a doctor, she would never be referred to as Mrs. Fred Wechsler – she was Doctor Helene Wechsler, and there was no question about it. So, within the three generations, the shift from the woman being a tagalong as a physician to being a primary in her role is very apparent.

As we see the reemergence of the feminine in the field of medicine, we also begin to become aware of the path that conventional medicine has taken.

When I was president of the American Holistic Medical Association in 1982, I received a letter from one of our trustees, Walt Stoll, M.D., in which he gently reprimanded me for using the term "non-traditional" regarding our work. He suggested that we accept our position as the true traditionalists in medicine and that the current practice of medicine be termed "conventional." Walt's position was that medicine, as it is taught today, should be called conventional since it deals with scientific diagnosis and treatment of diseases and, in a sense, tends to alienate the human being.

The holistic physician of today, in reality, should be called the "traditional" doctor. Why? Because we are working with, and trying to understand, the total human being and how his or her lifestyle, thoughts and beliefs affect or create the illness or health. We, as holistic physicians, work with concepts and methodologies that are steeped in tradition.

We, in the field of holistic medicine, are doing the things that have always been accepted as the role of the traditional physician. Acupuncture and herbal medicine are certainly traditional; manipulation and massage have been known and used since the beginning of time; castor oil was used for Cleopatra by her physician; prayer, meditation and the laying-on-of-hands have been practiced by physicians for thousands of years. The power of healing associated with the sing of the Native American shaman has been important in that culture, along with many other healing techniques.

As traditional physicians we may use alternative healing techniques but we do not practice just alternative medicine. There are those aspects of medicine shared by both the traditional and the conventional disciplines, such as surgery and obstetrics. As we reinvent traditional medicine, we bring to those areas, for instance, the dimensions of the spirit and creative thinking, plus the modalities that are traditional in nature and often called "alternative."

It has been only in the last 100 years that traditional medicine has moved from the center of the stage with allopathic concepts of conventional medicine taking its place. It was in the early years of last century that the Flexner report was created and implemented, bringing medical education into the universities, which, in turn, formulated allopathic medicine into its present scientific, clinical format of today.

Certainly Imhotep, Hippocrates, Osler and the Biblical Luke all wrote about concepts that were clearly holistic. Maimonides, a Hebrew physician who lived from 1135 to 1204 A.D., said, "The physician should not treat the disease, but the patient who is suffering from it." In modern times, one of the great medical writers, Dr. Felix Marti-Ibanez, had this to say: "To be a doctor, then, means much more than to dispense pills or to patch up or repair torn flesh and shattered minds. To be a doctor is to be an intermediary between man and God."

As holistic physicians, let us not forget to claim our heritage as the real traditional physicians and accept the feminine face of medicine. These experiences are all part of my evolving timeline and history, and speak to the physician within each of us.

What Living Medicine does is to bring the life essence back into the established practice of medicine. Holistic medicine merged body, mind and spirit together. Living Medicine now infuses life itself into the practice of holistic medicine. It brings traditional medicine back to life and asks conventional medicine to become a living thing.

A great portion of my library houses books containing the information derived from the Edgar Cayce readings. In fact, huge areas of open space would open up on my shelves if I were to remove the material that has its roots in his work.

Edgar Cayce was a humble man who died in 1945 in Virginia Beach, Virginia. He is, perhaps, the most well-known and certainly well-documented psychic of our time. Cayce had the astonishing ability to move into an altered state of consciousness and contact the unconscious mind of the person for whom he was giving "a reading." More than 14,000 of these readings have been studied in detail and are housed at the Association for Research and Enlightenment, or A.R.E., in Virginia Beach.

For most of his lifetime, Cayce received requests for help with all kinds of problems – physical, mental, emotional and spiritual – from people who would write to him. Then, from this state of altered consciousness, he gave them readings explaining why the condition existed and what they could do about it. Some 9,000 of the readings were termed "physical," which meant they dealt with health problems. These included aspects of disease and therapeutic modalities that were sometimes unusual and even those considered very conventional at that time. The depth and breadth of this work has provided an ongoing source of information and inspiration for me. For example, the Edgar Cayce material brought the concept of reincarnation into focus for me.

When the idea of reincarnation became part of my thinking, I already had four children. Two of them, Helene and David, however, came into our home after I had learned something about how to prepare for pregnancy, with the concept of reincarnation giving me a broader concept of life.

Helene and David are two years apart. Both of them talked about possible past lives as easily as they discussed their classmates in school. But, it seemed that emotions always played their part, and Helene picked on David from the time he was little. They became the best of friends in their teens, but those early years were sometimes stressful.

One day, when Helene was about eight and David was six, they had one of their usual spats. Most of the time, Bill and I let them settle these things by themselves. But this time it seemed to be getting a little bit deeper, so I took David aside to talk to him while Bill took Helene. Bill said to her, "Now, Helene, you know you chose this family, and sooner or later you're going to have to learn to get along with David or you'll come back as his wife, or something." Quick as a flash she responded, "Yes, I know that, but that's before I knew David was coming."

When Bill McGarey and I first became interested in the Edgar Cayce material, it was very difficult for us to understand Cayce's approach to diseases. Due to our training in medicine, we looked for a diagnosis of the specific diseases and a therapy that would help to treat them. Edgar Cayce's approach to healing did not fit this model.

It was only after repeated, gentle pushing from Cayce's son, Hugh Lynn Cayce, that we began to understand this approach was not focused on the disease but on the person and physiological principles inherent in maintaining health. He talked about a balance between the kidneys and the liver, coordination between the sympathetic and the parasympathetic nervous system, the importance of the lymphatic system, and of the use of castor oil as vital to the proper functioning of the lymphatic system.

When we finally understood this, we were able to comprehend that the use of the castor oil pack for problems as divergent as epilepsy and a sprained ankle had a great deal to do with vibrational energy and with the optimal functioning of the lymphatic system. Edgar Cayce's readings identify diseases but treat people individually.

I have been asked repeatedly if I treat multiple sclerosis or breast cancer, or some other disease by itself. My answer to that is, "No. I do, however, treat people who happen to be struggling with multiple sclerosis or breast cancer or hepatitis, or whatever their issue might be."

It is interesting that the only diseases mentioned in the Bible, as far as I know, are leprosy and epilepsy. Jesus did not treat diseases; he healed people. When the woman with the bloody flow touched the hem of his garment, there was no mention of fibroids or menopause or cancer or any other disease entity. It was simply the symptom.

The Bible does not describe the man with the withered arm who was healed on the Sabbath as having polio or brachial plexus syndrome or any other disease process. Again, it was simply the symptom. Jesus, of course, as the Great Physician, was able to see beyond the symptom to the issues that particular soul was dealing with. The healing came about when he said, "Your sins are forgiven you. Go and sin no more."

Forgiveness breaks the bonds holding the blocked energy that causes illness. The Chinese say that pain comes from blocks in the chi energy while acupuncture allows it to flow again, relieving the pain. Castor oil packs clear the lymphatics so that the lymph can flow without obstruction. Cayce recommended the wet cell and impedance device as instruments effective in balancing and moving energy within the body to initiate healing in the various parts of the body. We know, psychologically, if we allow ourselves to be blocked emotionally, it becomes very difficult for us to proceed with life. Fear and anger block energy. Laughter, music and beauty shift that block and allow the energy to move again.

When we translate these concepts in the context of the life energy that rises along the path of the kundalini through the seven spiritual centers, then we begin to see that – if the energy becomes stuck at the level of the adrenals where judgment, lack of forgiveness, anger and particularly fear reside – true healing does not manifest until the energy rises past the adrenals and up into the heart chakra where love, compassion and forgiveness dwell.

The Bible says, "God is love," (I John 4:8), and Jesus came to Earth to manifest the love of God in the flesh. It is when we, as individuals, are able to manifest the consciousness of the Christ, that healing of a true nature will come to us and to the Earth. Sometimes this means that, as in the case of the Apostle Paul, there will be a thorn in the flesh or some symptom that may not be eliminated. Yet, in spite of or due to our awareness of that problem, we are healed.

My library is probably the place where I learned more about patience and consistency than in any other room. I am not very much into the Computer Age, and the use of the computer has been a process in which I have often lost patience and have had trouble remaining consistent. However, the computer is still in my library. The importance of living life in the present, day by day, line upon line and precept upon precept, allows true healing to occur. It has to happen at a cellular level. It has to happen as an ongoing process.

These three words, *patience, persistence,* and *consistency,* are pivotal to understanding and working with the Cayce material. For years I have heard people complain that it is very difficult to understand, with long sentences, archaic language, and so on. But I know that if we put patience, persistence and consistency into action, we will be able to understand on a deeper level what Edgar Cayce had to say. Simply looking at and reading the words can be very confusing and does not begin to touch the wisdom available to us. We have to look deeper than the "fix-it" consciousness.

We all have times in our lives when patience becomes a necessary commodity. I have been experiencing this for the last five years, during which time my oldest daughter started writing my biography. All of that was fine and interesting. She completed the manuscript and we felt that the work was done. To our amazement, much of the work had, in reality, just begun.

Herein lies patience. The persistence and consistency represented part of getting the work done to that point. Then we were faced with releasing our control over the work. We had to turn it over to the publisher, editor, printer, cover designer and the bookbinder, with little or no control over the time involved to create the final product. If we thought it was going to take two months, it usually took four. If we were told that certain part of the process had been completed and we assumed that things would go faster, they did not. Finally, when we were told it had gone to the bookbinder and would probably take a couple of weeks – it took three months.

Now, in retrospect, the end product was well worth it, and our impatience with the process was only a waste of energy and totally unfruitful. But, if any of the steps along the way had been eliminated in order to fit our expectations, we would have had an incomplete product and, in reality, it would have been like having a premature baby.

Cayce said, "In patience, possess ye your souls." Impatience probably causes more strain and stress in our lives than any one thing. We get impatient with ourselves, with our loved ones, with life and with situations that do not go the way we think they should at that particular time. Our blood pressure rises; our anger builds; our adrenals get exhausted; and I even think we age faster.

If I had a lesson to learn while publishing a book, how much deeper and more profound the lesson would be when dealing with healing. We are impatient people by our very natures. We want to grow up too fast until we are older and then we become impatient with the aging process and want to be younger. True healing requires changes – physically, of the cellular and molecular structure; mentally, by changing our attitudes and thoughts; and spiritually, by attuning to the divine. If we try to bypass or speed up the process at any level, it is like interfering with a pregnancy and not allowing the baby to grow at its own rate and its own needs.

There is a story about a man who found a butterfly's cocoon. One day a small opening appeared. He sat and watched the butterfly for several hours as it struggled to force its body through that little hole. Then it seemed to stop making any progress. It appeared as if it had gotten as far as it could and could move no further. So the man decided to help the butterfly. He took a pair of scissors and snipped off the remaining bit of the cocoon. The butterfly then emerged easily. But it had a swollen body and small, shriveled wings. The man continued to watch the butterfly because he expected that, at any moment, the wings would enlarge and expand to support the body that would contract in time.

Neither happened! In fact, the butterfly spent the rest of its life crawling around with a swollen body and shriveled wings, never able to fly. What the man, in his kindness and haste, did not understand was that the restricting cocoon and the struggle required for the butterfly to get through the tiny opening were God's way of forcing fluid from the butterfly's body into its wings so that it would be ready for flight once it achieved its freedom from the cocoon.

Sometimes struggles are exactly what we need in our lives. If God allowed us to go through our lives without any obstacles, it would cripple us. We would not be as strong as what we could have been. We could never fly!

If we can begin to understand that life is a process, that everything we do is part of that process, and that we learn only as we accept the ongoing reality of the process, we then begin to relax and enjoy life. Patience and joy go hand-in-hand. It is hard to be impatient when you are laughing.

We are so accustomed to immediate success or healing that it remains very difficult for us to have patience with a healing that may take a long time. In order for true healing to happen, we must allow sufficient time and patience while working with the process.

Practicing persistence and consistency will bring a condition into reality. This is our conscious job, but then we must have patience to complete it. It is like planting a seed and then watering it. We do this consciously, but then we have to let it grow with patience. If we keep digging it up to see how it is coming along, we kill it. In Cayce's words, patience is "the impelling influence."

The library holds our memories, which can be accessed as we look for answers and search for therapeutic modalities.

In 1982 I was asked to speak as president of the American Holistic Medical Association at a conference for clinical psychologists in Washington, D.C. These represented the leaders and "teachers of the teachers" in this area, and 10,000 psychologists were expected for this international gathering. The president of the American Medical Association and I were scheduled to speak for thirty minutes each, and then we would open the session for questions.

I wrote to the AMA president twice on our gold-embossed stationery, suggesting we speak to each other beforehand to get a better sense of our talks. He never answered my letters. I was concerned by this because the AMA was considered such an important organization while the AHMA was just a fledgling one. The idea of facing that many psychologists in opposition to the president of the AMA was really intimidating. I asked my study group to keep me in their prayers constantly.

That weekend there was a meeting of the Association for Research and Enlightenment in Washington, D.C., where I was also a speaker. At the end of my talk, I asked the attendees to pray for me when I spoke to the psychologists. Then I left the A.R.E. meeting for the hotel where the psychologists were gathered. This was a Sunday afternoon, and Dr. Riel and I were scheduled to speak Monday morning. I decided to go down to the opening meeting of the organization so I would get a sense of what was expected and a feeling for the group itself.

I sat in the back row of this huge auditorium, feeling smaller and smaller, talking to God, and wondering what in the world I was to say. Finally, I felt that if I did not go back up to my room, I would just fall through the floor. I really asked for God's help so that I would say and do the best I could. Since I could not sleep, I picked up the Gideon Bible and turned randomly to Proverbs 11:14, which says, "Where no counsel is, the people fall: but in the presence of a multitude of counselors, there is safety." After reading this statement I said, "Thank you, God" and slept like a baby.

The next morning I had breakfast with Jean Ann Caywood, who was executive director of the AHMA. I was still feeling very insecure about the next hour. A woman approached us just as we were finishing breakfast and said, "Something terrible has happened. Dr. Reil was flying from Baltimore to Washington when his plane was caught up in a windstorm, so he had to turn back to Baltimore. He could not land. He will not be at the meeting."

This was a great relief to me. I had the whole hour to myself and was able to talk about holistic medicine. In closing, I told the group about Proverbs 11:14 and said, "And you, my friends, are a multitude of counselors." With that, they were on their feet for a standing ovation.

Group and individual prayers are surely answered one way or another; we just do not understand how. Sometimes our prayers are answered, and at other times God simply lets us know that the answer is "No." Or God answers in a form that we have not expected and maybe do not appreciate. Also, God's timing and our timing are not always the same.

With Dr. Reil, I would never have expected the prayers to be answered in that way. I have heard of snowstorms, hailstorms, and sandstorms, but have never heard of a windstorm during a short-distance flight, such as from Baltimore to Washington, D.C., that was so strong the plane had to turn back. I believe it is impossible to overestimate the power of prayer.

Memories are also found in our libraries. Habits are memories stored in our bodies while our bodies are the libraries for our thoughts and memories.

Two years ago when my sister Margaret was visiting me, we became aware of a mannerism that we both shared. Something would happen and, without saying a word, we would take one hand and just sweep it aside in a way that was exactly the same. We got to wondering why we did this because there did not seem to be any reason for it. We realized that it was usually at a time when we were responding to something that had taken place.

We wondered, "Why do we do this?" but had no answer. So we pondered, "Who do we know that used to do this?" and recalled that it was our mother. Our next question was, "Why did she do this?" We realized she did it when something happened that she chose not to give much energy or substance to. She would take her hand and just sweep it, essentially meaning: "Don't pay any attention," or "It doesn't make any difference."

What we learned through her actions and her words was a way of dealing with issues that could be irritating and confusing. We could just let them go by, accepting that they were there, and then release them with this movement of our hand. I know that I was able to deal with difficult situations in my life throughout the years by simply doing this one thing, even though I was not consciously aware of it.

When something happened that was uncomfortable, uncalled for or just unpleasant, instead of taking it into my heart and saying, "Oh my, that's terrible; that's very bad; I don't like it," I would merely let it go by and go on with what was important. Rather than focusing on what could be a real dilemma, my mother taught me to accept the reality that while problems do happen, sometimes it's just better to move on.

The Chinese do something very similar during Tai Chi. They take the energy that comes toward them and, instead of confronting it and making it a major problem, they move with it and let it go by. Since that time, I have talked to many of my patients about this technique and have found that it helps them deal with life's little irritations, which so often confuse them, conflict them, and cause deep problems.

Another mannerism that I have become aware of is the way I use my hands in times of conflict. If I have something that I disagree with and lift my hands with my palms out as I say, "No," it becomes an act of defiance or confrontation. But if I lift my hands and have the palms facing toward me, this motion can be translated to something like: "I don't think so;" or "That's not right;" or some other kind of statement that allows my opinion to be expressed and without representing an act of confrontation. It does not feel the same when the palm is facing toward me as it does when the palm is facing toward the person to whom I am speaking.

It also has been said that the eye of God is in the palm of our hand. So when I use this technique of turning my palm toward myself instead of facing the person that I am disagreeing with, I reclaim my own energy by having it come back to me without confronting the person. It allows us to have a conversation that is ongoing and healing instead of combative or destructive.

In my library of Living Medicine, I have memories that are stored away like my books on the shelf. I can take them out, look at them, read them and then put them back.

I remember being called away from the breakfast table one morning as a ten-year-old child in India because a snake charmer was in our front yard. He told us that he had a cobra in his basket that he had just caught and asked my father if he would like to see it. Being of a curious nature, he agreed, and the snake charmer told us all to stand back. The snake charmers in India use a technique of removing the fangs of the cobra in order to decrease the danger of working with them. This new snake had not been treated and, therefore, was potentially a great danger.

He put the basket with the cobra in front of him and, as he lifted the lid, immediately began to play his gourd flute. As quick as a flash, the cobra traveled a good 10 or 15 feet away. As soon as the first notes came out of the flute, the cobra immediately stopped, raised itself up, opened its hood, turned around and came back to stop right in front of the snake charmer's knee. Then it continued to weave gently back and forth as if hypnotized by the music.

The snake charmer stopped playing his flute to throw a blanket over the snake and put it back into the basket. Before he could get the blanket over the cobra, it struck and bit him on the index finger. The snake charmer proceeded to wrap the cobra up in the blanket and place it into the basket.

My father, being a physician, started to institute some emergency measures, but the snake charmer calmly said, "No, I can take care of this." He wrapped a pliable root around his upper arm as a tourniquet, reached into a small box and removed a small black object that resembled a stone. He placed it on the bitten finger and rested his hand on his knee. He then developed a severe tremor in his hand and began to sweat profusely. After five or ten minutes, the tremor quieted down and, finally, the black stone dropped off his finger. He picked up the stone, tapped it on his flute, and several drops of viscid fluid fell on the instrument, discoloring it.

My father was so fascinated with this whole procedure that he asked the snake charmer about the black stone. The snake charmer told him that it was the brain of a Himalayan tree frog, which had been slowly processed in heat so that it was carbonated. This was what all of the snake charmers in India used. They also knew that after receiving approximately 30 bites by a cobra, they needed to get out of the business because any further venom left in their system would cause chronic neurological damage.

The snake charmer took the black stone and placed it in his little box. He told us he would boil it in milk with spices before he put it away for future use. This whole scene was very vividly etched in my mind.

To my knowledge there has been little or no research done in areas such as this, yet detailed therapeutic techniques have evolved around the world to produce similar results.

It is interesting that the snake charmers have known since ancient times that thc toxins from the snake's venom that impact the nervous system could be alleviated by using nerve tissue from another reptile. This attracts the venom in such a way as to extract it from the nerves of the snake charmer. What is the energy that allows this "like attracts like" reality to manifest? This is truly energy medicine.

Another memory with a message for Living Medicine comes to mind when I look back to a time in November 1982. I participated in a lecture for The American School Health Association with a Navajo Indian medicine man, a Yacqui Indian Curander, a Viennese woman whose husband is a Western physician, her father who was a traditional Viennese physician and our own nurse-practitioner, Edna Germain.

The audience consisted of some 300 school nurses and education-related health professionals. It was an exciting morning because we found that all five of us were basically saying the same thing – namely, that in any tradition, healing comes from within each individual and, as people became involved in the healing arts, we developed various tools that perform similar tasks.

Each one of these people had years of training behind them, years of working with their own people and years of developing their own particular healing art. And each had been involved in successful healings through methods and modalities that, if nothing else, remain mysterious and unknown to us.

It occurred to me that in the West we have assumed an incredible arrogance, which says that the only real cures that work come from our own scientific model. This kind of presumptuousness closes doors, intimidates people and may set us back in consciousness instead of allowing us to move forward.

That same week, our small Casa Grande newspaper had a series of three extensive articles dealing with health care in our nation. The primary question was whether we have the moral right to decide on the use of our life-saving measures based on economics. The premise was based on the fact that many of the life-support measures amounting to billions of dollars are making it financially impossible for our country to continue with health care in its present state.

It was interesting to me that, this extensive series never addressed the individual patient's right to make the decision. The responsibility of the patients themselves for their own health care was not even considered, nor was the idea of "giving the body back to its rightful owner" even intimated. It failed to mention nutrition, exercise, spiritual attunement or the idea that individual people have not only the right but the responsibility to pay attention to their own health care.

Instead, the articles revolved around the concept that the physician was the one who made the decisions as to whether a person lived or died and that this was his or her responsibility. Unfortunately, government agencies and insurance companies are running out of funds trying to maintain this status.

I believe that, as physicians, we are not God and do not have the right to say whether a patient lives or dies. But we certainly have the duty to teach our patients how to take care of themselves and take responsibility for their own decisions. Physicians also need to assume responsibility for their own health.

We, as spiritual beings, know that death is not the end. It is more important to stimulate and awaken the spirit within all patients so they contact the physician within themselves and then use whatever modality is most suited to their needs. When physicians start taking this approach, then, perhaps, we will be working with true healing.

Since my library is a living space, it brings me right up to the present. I was given the opportunity to go back to the villages of northern India and Afghanistan for almost three months. In India I had the privilege of conducting physical exams and nutritional assessments for nearly 900 children in the homes for children of leper parents that my parents and my Aunt Belle had started more than sixty years ago. These are wonderful children who need all the help they can get since leprosy still remains a problem in India, despite medication and great strides taken to control it.

From India I went to Afghanistan to work with my brother, Carl, and Shukria Hussan, M.D., under the auspices of Future Generations. Since Afghanistan has been a war-torn country for the past thirty years, women and children, in particular, have suffered under these circumstances. The maternal mortality rate is higher in Afghanistan than any other place in the world.

It was my prayer that I might be able to help. We knew it was important for us to be able to talk to older women who had experienced pregnancies in order to get some idea of why conditions were so bad. In order to do this, we were able to set up weeklong programs (after getting permission from the men in the villages) where we lived with the women in a secluded place. We had asked for two women from ten different small villages in Bamian district and thought that we could handle twenty very well in the house we had rented. To our surprise, fifty women showed up and we had to send twenty of them back since thirty was the absolute maximum number we could work with.

These women were mothers-in-law and some of them brought small children along with them, even nursing babies. They all had had between two and fourteen pregnancies. Most of them had lost from one to six children, and all of them had stories of deep suffering and pain.

We created histories for each pregnancy, including the children who had died. We had each woman tell her story of each pregnancy, delivery and postpartum course. These stories brought to light some very interesting conditions.

First, we were told that when a woman went into labor, she was not given anything to eat or drink until the baby was born. Second, there were certain food taboos that prevented pregnant women from eating "cold foods" throughout the pregnancy, including milk and eggs. Third, the delivery usually took place directly on a dirt floor by someone who had no training or understanding of the birthing process and hygiene.

These women were anxious to learn and soaked up the information hungrily. We had a wonderful time. In the middle of the week, some of the women got up and began dancing. I took pictures of them and, when I showed them to staff people of Future Generations, the men said, "Don't let their husbands see those pictures because they are not supposed to dance, laugh or have fun. If their husbands see these pictures, they will be severely punished."

I have heard from my brother and Dr. Hussan that a follow-up meeting with these women a month after we had been there was very exciting. Twenty-eight of the thirty women came back. They all said that as soon as they returned to their villages, they spent four days in the mosque with the other village women. The women who had not been able to participate in the workshop came to them asking what they had learned and how they could work together in their village.

They reported that deliveries had been successfully performed without starving the women and they began utilizing clean cloths for the delivery and proper cord-cutting procedures. Prior to this, the women had used any instrument available, including a stone, to cut the cord. This practice resulted in neonatal tetanus, which, of course, was one of the diseases that caused infant death. They said that they had done a lot to improve the hygienic conditions and had tried to improve nutrition. The work continues as women teach other women what they have learned.

The Afghani health system has established a program to train midwives, who are primarily young girls between the ages of sixteen and twenty. Unfortunately, this program has not been very successful because, once trained, the majority of these young girls are not interested in living in the back villages and doing this type of work. They prefer working in the towns and cities that offer better conditions.

This experience has been a rich and rewarding one for me, and I have many precious memories of these beautiful people. They continue to teach each other as they continue to learn, building their own library of knowledge and experiences.

Each of us has, within our psyche, our own personal library where we have stored our experiences. This offers us a place where we can access information, which allows us to continue to live and grow.

As physicians, our library allows us to share in the knowledge and healing aspects of the past as we evolve the healing techniques and concepts of life for the future. In this day and age, the computer has brought to our fingertips the availability of information and therapies that have never been readily accessible to us before. Within moments we can access the available therapies for any specific disease process and see how this interacts with other therapeutic modalities. We can access the patient's medical history, all of their medications and their latest vital signs.

Amazing technology becomes available to us as we learn to use it. In my lifetime, the science of medicine has advanced so far that it is truly amazing. Our challenge now is to take this incredible science and infuse it with life so that it truly can be used as the art of medicine. It is our job as physicians to be able to help the patient use this knowledge in their healing process, not be overwhelmed by it and terrified by so much information. This scientific information is such an awesome tool that we need to constantly be learning how to apply it in the art of medicine.

Chapter Six

The Bedroom

A central room in our house of Living Medicine is the bedroom. Whether situated in a two-million-dollar mansion or a mud hut, the bedroom is the place where only selected people are invited in. It is the place where the most intimate relationships are shared and where the most profound personal experiences take place.

We retire to our bedroom when it is time for us to move into that aspect of our life that our conscious and unconscious mind shares. Most of us in an average day spend about a third of our time in our bedroom. It truly is a holy of holies. Many of us actually have a small personal altar in our bedroom or just off to the side of it. Our bedroom furniture, whether it is an engraved canopy bed or a bedding roll, is our own personal furniture. This is truly our safe place.

One very important role of the bedroom is that it is the place for rest. When we are sick, that is where we tend to go. When it is time for sleep, we retire to our bedroom.

Over the years I have heard many complaints about sleep from my patients. They say things like: "It's three o'clock in the morning. I feel like I have not slept a wink, and I have a day that is going to be busy and active. What do I do?"

Sleep is so wonderful, so refreshing and so important. We all need to sleep. However, as we get older, our patterns change, and eight hours of sleep is not always as essential as it was when we were younger. Of all the complaints I have heard from patients, insomnia seems to be one of the most frequent for those in the older age group. I explain to my older patients that their level of sleep is different from when we they were young. As older adults, even when we have interrupted sleep, we still can awaken refreshed with an adequate night's rest.

I often find that my patients and I can get away with what I call "good downtime." This means that I am in bed and resting. I may not be sleeping, but my body is functioning and fairly comfortable. I am just not sleeping.

During this time I try to let my mind reminisce on the good things in my life rather than the traumatic. I try to take this time to be grateful, to say some prayers of gratitude, to pray for everybody that I can think of who is in my life at the present time or in the past. I try to think about the beauties that I have seen in my long life. If I can do this, I find that not only does time go faster while I am in bed, but I sometimes fall asleep. Even if I do not, I find myself refreshed and joyful.

If, however, I worry about something and begin to fret, or if I find myself angry, frustrated, or frightened about the future, I not only don't get any rest but wake up fatigued and irritable. This is particularly true if I start worrying about not sleeping. When I put my energy into the idea that I am in bed and am supposed to be asleep, but I am not sleeping, all I find myself doing is building up more and more anxiety. The more this happens, the less I sleep. The less I sleep, the more anxious I get, and I go round and round.

For some of my patients, it is helpful to get up and fix a cup of tea or sit down and read something relaxing and then go back to bed. Watching the news or a scary movie or reading a murder mystery certainly offers no help in getting to sleep.

Allowing the body to become more alkaline also helps. This can be done with a small amount of baking soda in water, an Alka-Seltzer, or ten drops of Glyco-Thymoline in a glass of water. In conjunction with alkalinizing the body, taking some calcium can offer relief because it helps to relax the muscles and, therefore, the body. Taking calcium-magnesium tablets with either Glyco-Thymoline or Alka-Seltzer at bedtime is frequently as good as a sleeping pill. Other people find that one Benadryl capsule helps them sleep.

It is best not to eat a heavy meal before going to bed. The activity of the intestinal tract at bedtime can be disconcerting and cause sleeplessness.

Let us not forget the castor oil pack! Place it over the upper right side of your abdomen. Apply heat if you are going to use it before going to bed. Keep it on for 60 to 90 minutes while relaxing, allowing the body, mind and spirit to come into balance. If time does not allow the hour before bedtime, it can be used without heat, and you can sleep with it for several hours or all night long. When you put it on, be aware it has been called the Palma Christi (The Palm of Christ). You are placing this healing, loving, quieting, divine energy over your liver and solar plexus. This is the area of the third chakra where we carry stress and judgments, as well as anger and resentment. Using the castor oil pack with its healing energy over this area allows us to move into a space of divine peace, and sleep comes more readily.

If we watch television in our bedrooms immediately before sleep, or if we have a digital clock or other electrical equipment (such as waterbed heaters) right next to us, this creates an electrical field around the body that can make it difficult to sleep. It is recommended to not only turn off the TV in the bedroom, but also to unplug it. Move your digital clock at least ten feet away from your bed. Turn off the heater on your waterbed when you are ready to go to sleep. Look outside your window. Are there high-tension wires near your home? They can cause electrical problems with your nervous system, making it difficult to sleep. Try to make your bedroom a comfortable, pleasant place where you like to spend time and you will be more apt to have a restful sleep.

I believe the most important thing in dealing with insomnia has to do with attitude and accepting ourselves where we are. Maybe as senior citizens, eight hours of sleep is not necessary, but eight hours of good downtime is regenerating and replenishing. As physicians, if we listen to our patient's stories, we can sometimes find a clue to their insomnia and help them deal with the issue, which could be more helpful than a sleeping pill.

Sleep is not the only thing our bedrooms are used for. My last two children were born in my bedroom. It is where I rocked my children to sleep and nursed them when they were tiny. It is where they jumped on our bed to waken us and romp with us in the morning. It is where my husband and I spent our own private time together. It is probably the place where the tenderest of all emotions and feelings are shared. Where else can we have a good cry or laugh until we cannot even sit up? For many people the bedroom is the most comfortable place for us when we die.

Living Medicine involves the very act of giving and receiving from the conscious to the unconscious and from one person to another. One without the other is not complete. This is even manifested in every breath we take. We release the carbon dioxide used by plants and we take in the oxygen.

Birth and death are like that. The woman has to release the egg from the ovary so the sperm, which the male has released, can be taken into the egg. It is no longer just an egg, but becomes an embryo. One statement from the Cayce material reads: "Ovulation is the law of nature. Conception is the law of God." The embryo has to be willing to let go of old patterns and develop new ones. If, at any place along the path, it decides to keep the old and not receive the new, it dies. In order to grow and to develop into a human child, the embryo has to be constantly, on a molecular level, willing to change in order to live.

During my stay in Yakalong, Afghanistan, the village women eagerly received information about their anatomy and physiology and what actually happens within the body when conception takes place. They were aware of how conception took place but after that had no idea what went on within their bodies. It was some miraculous process that kind of took care of itself.

As I explained to them the structure of the vagina, uterus, tubes and ovaries using a small blackboard and a piece of chalk, they became excited. The idea that the uterus was actually a muscular structure, which contracted like other muscles in order to allow the baby to be born, was fascinating to them. I told them about the egg leaving the ovary, traveling down the tube and implanting itself in the wall of the uterus after it was impregnated by the sperm, which had traveled up the vagina and into the uterus.

One woman asked, "How many eggs?" I said, "One and that egg gets to choose which sperm it wants." Upon hearing these words, the women put their shoulders back and held their heads high, empowered by the realization that they actually, within themselves, had the power to choose which sperm was to impregnate their egg. This knowledge boosted their self-respect and strength.

When the time comes for the baby to be born, there must be a letting go of the comfort and security of the womb, the bedroom. The baby comes out into the world where she will have to breathe and eat and get rid of waste on her own. No longer can the mother do this for the baby. For the rest of the baby's life, she must be willing to give and receive on all levels – physically, mentally and spiritually. Only as she is willing to do this will she continue to grow, perhaps not taller or wider, but as new cells are constantly formed and destroyed. She breathes in and out; food goes in and out; muscles contract and relax. And when all of this stops, she dies. Then she releases the physical so the soul can continue its journey.

When we were in England with an A.R.E. group led by Hugh Lynn Cayce in 1969, a psychic by the name of Ronald Beasley spoke to us. He drew a picture of the auras surrounding different people. Some individuals had auras forming smoothly at the top while others had auras that were twisted at the top. I asked Ronald, "Why the difference?" and his response was that the ones whose auras were twisted were the people whose souls had not been properly tucked in with care when they were born.

To me this was very important. I truly believe the emotions and thoughts of those present at birth or death impact the type of experience for the soul making the transition. If, when a baby is born, there is joy and jubilation, that soul enters into this Earth with a feeling of being accepted and wanted. If, on the other hand, there is grief and dismay, the soul may feel unwanted and rejected. This can cause confusion and trauma, which that soul may struggle with all of his or her life.

I have a patient who is in her mid-fifties and the third child in a family in which the first two siblings were boys. When she was born, her father was unable to make it to the hospital and, even if he had been there, he would not have been allowed in the delivery room. When he did arrive at the hospital, the nurse informed him that he had a baby girl. His response was, "That's not possible. We don't have girls in our family." He said it as a joke but, in reality, he insisted that the nurse remove the baby's diaper so he could be sure that she was a girl and not a boy.

Every year on her birthday, he has repeated this story because he thinks it is funny. He consciously did no harm and did not reject her. But, as a newborn, she felt that her father not only rejected her as a person but also her sexuality and who she was as she came to this Earth. This has caused problems her entire life with relationships and with her own acceptance of who she is.

In the work that I have done with newborns, it has become ever clearer that the attitudes and emotions of the people surrounding the baby at birth are indelibly etched into her soul pattern. Having just been removed from the secure environment of the uterus where everything was provided, she now has to deal with other people's emotions on her own.

It is apparent with this woman that exposing and rejecting sexuality caused deep trauma. Fortunately, she understands this and has worked with it all her life. Others who have been either rejected or traumatized at birth may or may not know that this struggle leaves deep scars. Fortunately, emotional pain can be dealt with using techniques of rebirthing.

A friend of mine, who has struggled her whole life with feelings of insecurity and lack of a strong sense of personhood, told me that, when she was born, she was very thin and wrinkled. Thinking she was ugly, her mother covered her up with a small towel when anybody came to visit. This went on for many months and has become a "family joke" through the years.

People have laughed about it and thought it was very funny. In reality, this newborn little girl was so traumatized by her mother's actions and by the persistent, repeated telling of this "funny" story that she continues to feel rejected and unable to truly appreciate her own beauty. She is now sixty years old and a fine-looking woman, doing wonderful work as a counselor in the local high school. With this type of trauma to a person's psyche, we truly need to listen to life stories in order to find the root cause of some of our problems.

My daughter's youngest son was born in her bedroom and I had the privilege of delivering him. The people in attendance were, of course, her husband, and our Navajo nurse, Ernestine. Ernestine had had three children herself but had never been involved in a delivery for another woman. Things were going along quite well until the contractions became really severe and Helene was in hard labor. All of a sudden, Ernestine began jumping up and down around the room and waving her hands. I said, "What in the world are you doing?" and she said, "Navajo blessing! Navajo blessing!" and continued until she was through with her Navajo blessing. I know that this activity in that bedroom influenced the baby as he was born and for the rest of his life. It certainly was part of the sacred experience that the rest of us shared.

During a delivery if our whole focus is on killing, even killing the pain of childbirth, we may even accentuate killing by centering our attention on it. When we try to hang on to something that no longer serves its purpose, we create a block that results in pain. I have worked many hours with my obstetrics patients, having them move into the pain of the contraction, breathe with it, relax with it, not tighten up against it and fight it. We can use music or color or their husband's hands to apply pressure in the area where the pain remains greatest.

The mother can shift the pelvis into a more acceptable position, helping herself and the baby to move down and out. Sometimes a chant helps – anything that allows her to participate in the whole process. When a woman is able to do this, she needs much less pain medicine and less intervention. If she rides the wave of pain like a surfer rides the ocean waves, she will move with the energy of life and love. It is when we fight against the movement of life that pain becomes more severe.

During the years I was doing home deliveries with Barbara Brown, a registered nurse, midwife and nurse practitioner, we created the Baby Buggy, a mobile unit equipped to transport mother or baby if it became necessary. One of us would drive the Baby Buggy to the home of the mother in labor and have available IV solutions and equipment as needed for the delivery.

During one of these deliveries, Barbara worked with a young woman who had been involved in a religious group in which meditation played a central role in their spiritual activity. Therefore, she not only knew how to meditate but had spent many hours doing so. Therefore, she had not really accepted the fact that there might be pain and discomfort associated with the labor.

The patient became more and more distraught because she felt like she could not get herself into the meditative state she had been counting on to get her through the delivery.

Throughout this time the cervix was not dilating; it stayed at one centimeter and for several hours she remained in good hard labor with no progress whatsoever.

Finally, Barbara remembered the patient worked with meditation and knew how to chant. She realized that if this woman could come up with a chant that would work for her, then maybe she could move past the block that her pain was causing and get on with the delivery. So Barbara said, "Now, dear, I want you to start chanting, Open lotus, lotus open, open lotus, lotus open." The young woman immediately knew how to do that and began chanting. Within a few hours, the cervix opened to complete dilatation.

Now it was time to push but the patient was not emotionally ready. Trying to help, Barbara suggested that pushing the baby out was like having a large bowel movement. This young woman did not want her baby to be compared to a bowel movement. Barbara recognized that she needed another chant. The chant that she came up with was, "Down and out, down and out." With this chant the young woman was able to push and delivered the baby spontaneously.

For millennia, women have worked with other women in the birthing process. They even have created a birthing dance called "the belly dance." Pregnant women did this dance throughout pregnancy to keep the pelvis mobile and alive. The baby did not get stuck in one position so that he had to be pushed out or extracted. There were certain dance positions and movements that helped the process and, during labor, women would dance around the birthing mother as she participated in the dance as best she could.

When men became obstetricians, they felt it was their duty to help "stop the pain," so medications were created. They thought the mother did not feel the pain if medicated. In reality, women did feel pain, but medication dulled the memory of it and would not allow the women to work with the pain effectively.

When medicated, the action of fighting against the pain causes fear to be the dominant emotion. Muscles tighten, and the women feel alone in "the valley of the shadow of death." The baby is born with more difficulty to themselves and to the mother. Sometimes the mother will not know that the baby has been born for many hours.

I did not know I had a son with my first delivery until twenty-four hours after he was born. Then I was too groggy to really respond and bond with him. The whole birthing process was something to fight against. This, of course, does not mean that there aren't times when surgery and medication are needed, but these are the exceptions.

Metaphorically, it is not a far stretch to think of the uterus as the bedroom for a baby while preparing for birth. We now know that many babies can hear what is going on in the life of the mother just as we, in our bedrooms, know what is going on in the rest of the house.

The whole process of labor remains mysterious for many people. My trip to Afghanistan helped me realize that these wonderful women knew nothing about it. They had no idea what was in their bedroom. As we talked, they were filled with great joy when they realized that the cervix had to open up enough so that the baby could come through before pushing.

Prior to gaining this knowledge, if the mother did not have enough strength to push the baby out, they would put severe pressure on the abdomen from the outside. Sadly, this happened often since the woman in labor was given nothing to eat or drink as soon as she went into labor and until the baby was born. Using external pressure to force the baby out causes tearing of tissues and severe bleeding, and represents one of the major causes of maternal mortality among these women.

As difficult as this was to hear and deal with, when I came back to the U.S. I was horrified after talking to a physician friend who said that the Caesarian section rate is up to thirty-seven percent of all deliveries in our country. When I heard this, I realized that what we are doing is in essence the same as the Afghani women are doing.

In this country we are also using external means to extract the baby. The difference is that, with Caesarian sections, many times it represents a matter of convenience instead of necessity. The Afghani women used external means because they were ignorant of the physical aspect of delivering a baby. We are using external means because we are ignorant of the emotional and spiritual aspects of delivering a baby. This ignorance, I am convinced, is causing problems that we do not even comprehend at this point. The difference between what we do and the way the Afghani women give birth is that we have the ability to sew the tissues back together again and they do not. We may think that the Afghani way of birthing is terrible but, given in our country that many times Caesarians are used for convenience sake only, who are we to judge when it is ignorance causing intervention?

In the November 20, 2006, issue of *Time* magazine, an article titled Ahead of Their Time by Coco Masters states:

> *In the U.S., one of the richest countries in the world, the number of babies born too early keeps going up – and with all their medical savvy, doctors can't figure out why. Today*

nearly 13 out of every 100 births are premature, an increase of 30 percent over the past 20 years. Part of the rise is due to the advent of modern fertility treatments, which caused a sharp jump in the number of twins, triplets and higher multiples – most of whom are born early. But it turns out that 83 percent of preemies in the U.S. are singletons whose prematurity can be caused by any number of factors, including bacterial infections, ruptured membranes, cervical abnormalities, high blood pressure, stress, inflammation and the effects of smoking and alcohol consumption.

So now doctors are starting to rethink their approach to the problem of prematurity, which is defined as being born at least three weeks shy of a full 40-week term. Rather than focusing primarily on the care of the newborn, they are going back to the beginning of pregnancy and paying a lot more attention to the health of the mother.

These premature babies are all struggling to learn what full term babies already know – that is, how to keep warm, how to breathe, how to suckle, how to swallow. In spite of the fact that today's neonatalogists can ensure the survival of 95% of the infants born before term, these babies are faced with long term complications ranging from mental retardation and cerebral palsy to hyperactivity and respiratory disorders. What these doctors are finding out is that the attention needs to go to helping the mother have a more healthy pregnancy which, or course, focuses on good diet, exercise, healthy living conditions, lack of alcohol or tobacco and good exercise – just the plain ordinary things that make for a healthier life.

A major emphasis is on educating the public about the dangers of preterm labor – and reminding physicians that a vacation, for instance, isn't a good-enough reason to schedule an early delivery. The assumption: if mothers knew the real risks of prematurity, they would be less likely to request induced labor or a C-section and would stick out the pregnancy to term.

But as Dr. Henrietta Bada, chief of neonatology at the University of Kentucky, explains, those last few weeks in the womb are critical for a newborn's development. The health risks for a baby born at week 35, she says, are more like those of a baby born at week 30 than one born at week 37. "The perception is that a big baby – even if he's premature – is going to act like a term baby. He's not.

On the weekend of November 10, 2006, there was a conference in Mesa, Arizona, entitled "The Baby Summit," the work of an international prenatal and perinatal psychology organization that deals with issues regarding pregnancy and deliveries. I have known about the work of this organization for many years and regard it highly.

Since I was one of the keynote speakers, I had the opportunity to talk to the whole group, addressing my concern about the problems the women in Afghanistan were having. I mentioned the work that I had done in Tibet with Future Generations in 1990 and my own work here in the United States. I commented that I was horrified to learn that our Caesarian section rate was 37 percent and most of these were elective C-sections.

A woman in the audience stood up during the question-and-answer period and said she was from Mexico where 85 percent of the hospital deliveries are C-sections. Another woman from Brazil said her country's hospital delivery rate for C-sections was 90 percent. And, much to my horror, a woman from Iran said that their C-section rate in hospitals was 100 percent.

I was appalled as were most of the people in attendance. I almost cannot comprehend this; every reason I come up with makes no sense and I have come up with many. The underlying cause must be that we, as women, have lost our sense of reality. We know how to have babies; we are built to have babies; and we need to trust ourselves and our own bodies. Our own babies know how to come into this world. That has been possible ever since the beginning of our time, and now why we think intervention is needed to this extent is unreal.

And C-sections are not without their complications. I am not talking about those that are indicated, which is probably about 5 percent of the deliveries.

Another lecture at the Baby Summit featured Joel M. Evans, M.D., founder and director for The Center for Women's Health in Darien, Connecticut, an assistant clinical professor at Albert Einstein College of Medicine and senior faculty at the Center for Mind/Body Medicine in Washington, D.C. He outlined the complications attached to C-sections:

Short-Term Complications:

Death: 0.04 per 1,000 vaginal births compared with 0.53 per 1,000 Caesarian deliveries;

Thromboembolism: 4 to 7 times increase

Hemorrhage: Risk increases with number

Infection – Endometritis: 5 to 85 percent, depending on clinical situation

Wound Infections: 2.5, or 16 percent

Surgical Injury: Bladder most common 0.28 percent

Need for a Hysterectomy: 13 times more likely

Pain: All women (100 percent) having a Caesarian require narcotics versus 11 percent of vaginal deliveries. Narcotics impact initial bonding between the mother and the newborn, breastfeeding rates and maternal functioning postpartum and possibly increase the risk for postpartum depression. Women undergoing surgical evaluation for chronic pelvic pain were 3.7 times more likely to have had a prior Caesarian delivery

Poor Birth Experience: Long-term risks – Re-admission to the hospital 80-percent increase

Adhesion Formation: Contributes to ectopic pregnancy and small bowel obstruction.

Risks to the Newborn:

Breathing Difficulties: TTN which probably results from a failure of the mechanisms to resorb fetal lung fluid that is typically triggered during vaginal birth. A review of nearly 30,000 births found that the incidence of

TTN is about three times more common after elective Caesarian delivery than after vaginal delivery.

Asthma: In 40,000 children, those delivered either by planned or unplanned Caesarian were approximately 30 percent more likely than those delivered vaginally to have been admitted to the hospital for asthma during childhood.

Failure to Breastfeed: A study of more than 580,000 women in California found that mothers who underwent planned or unplanned Caesarian deliveries were nearly twice as likely to have breastfeeding difficulties compared with those who delivered vaginally.

With all of these risks, why in the world would a woman choose a C-section rather than a normal vaginal delivery? I know full well there are times when a Caesarian will save the lives of the baby and the mother, and that is a completely different issue.

What the mother thinks and feels directly affects the baby. People who have been regressed to life in the uterus can tell many stories of things that happened during their intrauterine life. The baby is a conscious living being, and the uterus itself responds to the mother's emotion. The placenta knows its work and does it very well.

I had a pregnant patient come in to see me long after I stopped delivering babies because she had questions about the pregnancy. At seven months she began to spot and was told that she had a placenta previa, which meant that the placenta was covering the cervix, or mouth of the uterus. In order to deliver the baby, she would probably need a C-section. She had been told to go home and get off of her feet.

I added two recommendations: one, that she use the castor oil pack over her lower abdomen without heat as much of the time as she could tolerate it; and, two, that she visualize the placenta moving off of the cervix and up onto the uterine wall. We know that the placenta does move and travel throughout the inner wall of the uterus, so I suggested she consciously visualize this happening while resting in bed.

She began doing what I prescribed, and the bleeding stopped. When the ultrasound was repeated a month later, the placenta had moved completely off of the cervix and up into the uterine wall. She carried the baby to full term and delivered a healthy 10-pound, redheaded little boy.

I spoke with actress Lindsay Wagner one day when she was pregnant with her second child. She had just returned from a class given by her childbirth instructor for children who were expecting a new brother or sister in their family. The class used charts, pictures and diagrams of the developing pregnancy, both from the perspective of someone on the outside watching and that of the baby developing on the inside. Among the illustrations was a picture of the umbilical cord as it attached to the baby in utero from its origin in the placenta. When Wagner's son Dorian saw this, he said, "That looks like a tree." As Lindsay thought about this, she realized that it did, indeed, resemble a tree – a truly universal symbol.

Every single one of us born into this dimension has spent close to nine months in the uterus with nothing to perceive except the walls of the womb, our own hands, our own feet and this amazing structure from which we receive our nourishment and a great deal of information. The structure itself is like a tree, with the placenta as its roots, the cord as its trunk and the developing baby as its limbs and fruit.

The more I thought about it, the more it seemed to me that we have a wonderful opportunity to look at this symbol, the tree of life. From ancient times it has had its roots deep in the ground and its limbs reaching up to the heavens. Its fruit grows gradually, ripens and then much like the story of pregnancy and birth, drops to the ground to start the whole cycle over again.

We need to understand the continuity of life and the importance of nourishment that comes from the mother to the baby and from the divine to the child. It is interesting that God is referred to as the Father in heaven and Earth as the Mother. We are the children of this symbolic union of spirit and flesh. The tree of life then brings nourishment, both from the Earth and from the heavens. The heavens give life itself to the developing child, the fruit of the union of the sperm and the ovum. From the Earth, the child is nourished with oxygen, food, minerals and chemicals.

If the soil is poor, the tree does not develop well and frequently becomes sick. Good soil, on the other hand, creates health. Thus, a baby growing in the womb with the placenta actively bringing nutrients to it either grows in health and vigor or it becomes ill, depending on the food the mother eats, the water she drinks, the air she breathes and the healthy or unhealthy nourishment produced. It is also the spirit that nourishes the thoughts she thinks, the movies she watches, the emotions she feels, the joy she expresses, the hope and love, faith and gentleness. All of these become part of what the baby lives and grows with. If the mother is angry, afraid, jealous or working with other negative emotions, the baby derives its nourishment from that environment, and the tree of life also can be blighted.

It is exciting to consider the wonderful opportunity that any mother has to nourish her baby in the way that God nourishes us.

During pregnancy, what you eat, what you think and what you pray for all become part of the consciousness of the growing fetus.

Women actually deal quite well with pain most of the time during labor. What they do not manage well is fear and abandonment. If a woman has support during labor, she can handle the pain much better than if she feels alone and abandoned.

Rabbi Herbert Weiner, who was a friend of ours for many, many years, told us a story about the angel of forgetfulness. He said that the Kabala identifies an angel who is present at the birth of every child. The angel touches the child on the upper lip, creating an indentation. This is the angel of forgetfulness. The baby forgets what s/he has known during the gestational period and is born with a clean slate. In my experience, there are many children now who must have been touched very lightly because they do remember and are aware of what transpired in utero and prior to the pregnancy.

For many years husbands were not allowed in or anywhere near the delivery room. Although my husband was a physician, my first four children were born without his presence. Therefore, I had my last two children at home so I could be in charge of who was present.

During the sixties and early seventies, many women wanted to have their babies at home or, at least, have their husbands in the delivery room. Husbands also wanted to be present. Since this was not acceptable in any of the Phoenix hospitals, we started a campaign in which my pregnant patients called the hospitals and asked if their husbands could be present in the delivery room. This went on for a period of twelve years until, finally, Memorial Hospital began to allow husbands in the delivery room. Of course, birthing rooms are now very well-equipped and families can be present.

I will never forget one delivery in which a mother was having her seventh child and all of the other six children and her husband were present for the birth. As soon as the baby was born, they all spontaneously began to sing "Happy Birthday to You."

A friend has created a school for autistic children primarily because she has an autistic son and there was no educational facility for children with this problem near where she lives. In her research she found that a great number of mothers with autistic children had some very severe emotional or physical trauma when they were four months pregnant. She remembered that, at the time she was four months' pregnant with her autistic child, her husband was having an affair with another woman. She subsequently had to live with her mother-in-law, who was very domineering and difficult person. While we really do not know what causes autism, this offers an interesting piece of information that should warrant further research.

During labor, a mother's thoughts and emotions are probably more at one with her total being – body, mind and spirit – than almost any other time in her life. What she thinks, what she believes and what she has recognized about life itself can and is more readily manipulated and attuned.

I had a patient who suddenly began hemorrhaging after childbirth. It was very profuse, and I knew that we had to get an IV started immediately. Every time we put the needle in, her veins collapsed. I remembered that she had said she preferred no intervention whatsoever in the delivery. She wanted to do it "naturally" without IV's or anything external in her body. It appeared to me that she was, in her unconscious state, creating a condition that resulted in us not being able to get an IV started. I also realized that, if she had that kind of control over her body, she might be able to stop the bleeding. So I said to her, "Linda, I want you to stop this bleeding, and I want you to stop it *right now*. You have control over your veins. You can control this. I want you to stop it *right now*." Within two minutes, the bleeding stopped.

Through the years, as I have worked with people who are being born and people who are dying, I have constantly been impressed with the fact that birth and death represent different sides of the same coin. In both situations, our souls choose the time for this transition, the place and the people present. I think it is important for us to understand that anyplace a baby is born or a person dies becomes holy ground. When it is time for the baby to "awaken" or be born, s/he then moves through the door and out into life. This movement through the birth passage is so similar to that of people who have had near-death experiences that it poses an interesting correlation.

Elisabeth Kübler-Ross, who was a patient of mine in Scottsdale, tells the story of the feeling she had *in utero*, the feeling of being squashed and hardly able to move – as if someone was sitting on her. This is not a death story but a birth story. Elisabeth was the first of triplets, and I would suppose the other two were perched on her shoulders most of the time waiting to be born. She also remembered how much she appreciated the love, tenderness and the warmth of the physician's hands as she and her sisters were ushered into the world.

Last year I was talking to a fifty-year-old Presbyterian minister. I had delivered him in Ohio and had seen him only occasionally in the years in between. He told me that all through his life he had remembered something which he had been unable to identify – a feeling, a sensation, a knowing. He finally identified this experience when he was present at the birth of his first child. He knew there was a time when everything he had experienced up until that point was shifting. He was being squeezed and propelled forward in a way that he had no control over. It was something unavoidable. He was moving through the darkness toward the light. He remembered when the pressure began to ease off and he moved into the light. There was great jubilation and excitement in the world he came into. I remember his birth very clearly. His parents had three daughters and were truly jubilant when he arrived.

Our souls seem to know that there comes a time when we let go of the old in order to move into the new. At birth, we move into the body, the vehicle through which we will find expression during this lifetime. In death, we let go of that particular vehicle and move into a dimension where our soul will express itself. In both, we move through a dark tunnel, propelled by a force that we seem to have little conscious control over, almost as if we are squeezing out the old in order for the new to enter. In both situations, we are moving toward the light.

The people who are with us at the time of our birth and at the time of our death are ones who the soul has chosen to have there. Time after time we hear stories of a parent who could not die until a certain child was present. I have had the same experience in delivering babies.

Things may look new, feel new and sound new as we are born. On the other hand, when we die and let go of the five senses, we move into sensations of a higher vibration that probably seem very new to us.

As we make this transition, we respond to those who are there to receive us and, in either case, whether it is the arms of the mother and father on this plane or the presence of God on the other, we will move into and behold the presence of love. When we are born, we breathe in the air and life; when we die, we exhale the air and breathe in the spirit. When we are born, the umbilical cord is cut, separating us from our mother so we become a separate individual. When we die, the silver cord is cut separating us from Mother Earth, and we become an individual spirit. Those who have had near-death or out-of-the-body experiences are aware of the presence of the silver cord and that, if it was severed, they would not be able to return to their bodies.

In the United States, you need certificates for both birth and death.

Abortion represents a topic that is always explosive in nature as the pros and cons of the subject come into view. I have difficulty trying to come to some sensible conclusions about the issue. The spontaneous abortion is no real psychological or ethical tug-of-war, but when it comes to an induced end to a pregnancy, there are literally thousands of well-meaning men and women on both sides of the dividing line. And I have been torn between the two warring factions.

In my mind, as the concept of the continuity of life grew in its reality and the pieces started to fall into place – that is, how we have no beginning and no end as spiritual creatures; how we choose our parents; how we may see what lies ahead, no matter what it may be; how experiences serve our growth and understanding – I began to feel a bit better about abortion when it was really needed. The idea of reincarnation helped.

But, I still had a problem with women who wanted an abortion because it was convenient, or because the pregnancy was embarrassing or threatening the stability of a marriage. These things did not make sense to me since I always adhered to the principle of sticking with something I had started.

One day, however, a new awareness dawned in my consciousness, and the business of abortion became more understandable. Not that I would have an abortion myself, in my present level of awareness; however, I can see that it is frequently reasonable, understandable and the "right" thing for a woman to do. (I will not get into that definition of "right"). This new light dawned with a story one of my patients told me some time ago.

A mother had a four-year-old girl named Dorothy whom she would take out to lunch occasionally. During one such lunch, as they were talking about various things, the child began to shift from one subject to another. Suddenly Dorothy said, "The last time I was a little girl, I had a different mommy!" She then began talking in a different language. Her mother quickly retrieved a pencil from her purse and copied down what her daughter said as nearly as she could understand it.

Then Dorothy continued: "But that wasn't the last time. Last time, when I was four inches long and in your tummy, Daddy wasn't ready to marry you yet, so I went away. But then, I came back." Her eyes lost that faraway look and she began chatting again about four-year-old matters.

The mother was silent. No one but her husband and the doctor knew that she had become pregnant about two years before she and her husband were ready to get married. When she was four months pregnant, she decided to have an abortion because her husband-to-be was not ready to become a father.

When the two of them did get married and both were ready to have their first child, the same entity evidently made its appearance. The little girl was saying, in effect, "I don't hold any resentment toward you for having had the abortion. I understood. I knew why it was done, and that's okay. So here I am again. It was an experience. I learned from it, and you learned from it. So now, let's get on with the business of life."

Perhaps the child did not have that kind of vocabulary, but that was in essence what was being said and related to the mother. It does throw a new light on abortion, doesn't it? Every experience is individual, and not all abortions have this kind of circumstance surrounding them. With this experience, I could see how things were different than I first thought. With birth and death, what we are dealing with is consciousness and the reality of consciousness.

Years ago I had a wonderful couple as patients who were in their nineties. Esther had a stroke and remained in the hospital for several weeks, unresponsive and connected to IV's. One day her daughter, a nurse who had worked with hospice and home nursing, came to the hospital room and pulled up a chair next to her mother's bed. She said, "Ma, if you want to die, it's all right; you can die. You've had a good life and, if this is your time, it's all right for you to go. But, if you want to live, you open your mouth and you start eating now, because Dad and I will take care of you and take you home. But you have to cooperate and you have to open your mouth and start eating."

Then she sat back and, after about fifteen minutes, her mother's mouth began to move, and she was able to give her some water. Gradually, she began to take sustenance and, within another week, they were able to take her home.

Esther lived for another six months at home and then quietly died in her sleep. Harry lived to be 104. When he was 102, I asked, "How are you doing, Harry?" He replied, "Just fine. My parents take care of me." I said, "What do you mean – parents?" He said, "Father Time, Mother Nature – they take care of me." He too, died peacefully in his sleep.

What we are really talking about is the movement of consciousness in birth and death. Some stories about real people help us to understand this aspect of life.

My mother, who was eighty-nine years old and suffering from severe osteoporosis, was living in our home. On the Thursday before Easter, she was in the garden admiring the petunias, which were in a riot of bloom and color. When she returned to the house, she came in through the door and saw on the table the work that my father had been doing. He was putting together his book and, on top of it all, was a poster my oldest brother John had created when he was coming home from school for the holidays. On the poster in bold print were the words "Homeward bound." Shortly after seeing that, she tripped and fell, fracturing her knee and multiple ribs on the left side. We got her into an ambulance and admitted into the Scottsdale Memorial Hospital. My father stayed with her all that evening, and the next day she said to him around noontime, "John, go get something to eat." He left to go down to the cafeteria for his lunch. After he left the room she passed quietly. It was Good Friday.

It was as if she could not leave with him being right there. They had enjoyed such a long, wonderful life together, and their lives were so entwined. It was hard for Dad to accept the fact that he was not there when she died. It was also hard for him to understand that she really could not go while he was there because his love was holding her. When we went out to the cemetery for her internment, there was a gentle rain falling and a double rainbow across the sky.

After Mother died, my father married my brother's mother-in-law. This was a little bit complicated since it then made my brother and his wife become, technically speaking, brother and sister. Their son was coming home from Harvard for the wedding and told his professors he needed a leave because his grandparents were getting married and they said, "Don't you think it's about time?"

Dad and Mother Daniels both enjoyed long, good, wonderful marriages, and now they were in a position where they could actually play. Neither one of them had ever taken the time just for that. They traveled for two years. Dad played shuffleboard and chess and puttered with tools and woodwork. Mother Daniels quilted. They shared a wonderful life together. It was almost like their first marriages had been the cake and this was the icing. Then Dad got sick and Mother Daniels knew that it was important for him to be in Phoenix with us and where Mother was buried. My husband and I thought maybe we would need a stretcher to get Dad off the plane. But no, my strong, staunch, zealous, Presbyterian father was able to pull all of his energy together and walk off the plane.

We then had to put him in the hospital because he was so sick. He was there for two weeks, and one morning Mother Daniels woke up and said, "I have to get to the hospital, and I have to get there now." My sister-in-law took her to the hospital and, as Mother Daniels walked in the door, she realized that Dad was just about ready to make the transition. She stood by his bedside, held his hand and sang, "When the roll is called up yonder, I'll be there." His lips moved with hers as she sang. She continued singing, "God be with you 'til we meet again," as he made the transition.

When I went to the hospital to bring her home, she said through her tears, "Don't you know, there's jubilation on the other side?!" I knew there was. I could just see my mother on the other side saying, "John, now, it's time for you to come on over. You just come right on over now." So, in full consciousness, he made the transition.

Lorraine Chase was the first psychologist to work with Art Linkletter on television. She and her husband were living in Scottsdale when she was diagnosed with lung cancer. Hospice was there to help her, and I made house calls.

About two weeks before she died, I went to see her, and she said to me, "I know I'm medicated, and I know it probably would be considered a hallucination; but I looked up yesterday and saw that door." She pointed to a door that had two small panels at the top, with larger panels on the bottom, making a cross on the face of the door. She said, "I looked up and I saw Jesus on that cross, and I said to him, 'Where have you been? I really, really have needed you.' He smiled and said, 'Right here.'" Then she said to him again, "I really need help, and I wish that you would help me." Smiling, he reached down from the cross to touch her, with one arm and his back still on the cross. She said, "How did you do that?" He smilingly said, "Velcro."

To me this is really important because here we have a woman who is dying and her sense of humor was so alive that she was able to joke with her God, who was also dying on the cross. What a powerfully wonderful way to make the transition!

Once, after a lecture, a woman came up to me and said that she was a hospice nurse. She had just experienced a situation in which an elderly mother was in a deep coma and surrounded by her grown children. One of the children said to her, "Mom, it's all right. Follow the light. Go to the light. It's all right." Suddenly, the woman opened her eyes, looked at her children and said, "Will somebody please turn off that light. I'm not ready to go yet."

I have had patients who, for one reason or another, have been confined to their homes, unable to function in the outer world. For people like this, particularly if they have been active and creative, this period of confinement presents a truly desperate time when their bedroom becomes a prison.

A friend of mine died last year. She was an eighty-eight-year-old nurse who had been vitally active in her career, impacting the growth and evolution of holistic medicine. For years she was known nationally for her ability to organize and present material. She was never presented with a project that she was unable to complete with great enthusiasm.

When she developed lung cancer, letting other people take care of her became really difficult. She was physically and mentally active until about two weeks before she died. During this time, as her condition deteriorated, the one thing she kept repeating to her daughter was, "I guess I really need to learn to accept help." All her life she had been the one who helped others, and now her final lesson was to learn to receive help – a very difficult but profound lesson. As she moved into a coma, periodically she would say to her daughter, "I need to accept help." Sometimes this is the single, most important lesson that we have to learn.

People who are confined to their bedroom look for ways in which they can still be useful.. As I listen to them, I realize that their physical problem can be a very difficult one.

But along with this is their inability to see how they can contribute anything at all to our world. Because of this, I tell them the story of my brother, Carl's, experience in Bhouton.

As I mentioned earlier, Carl is a physician who has been active with the World Health Organization all of his professional life. In 1962 he was invited by two physician friends to go to their country to see what could be done to improve the health of the people. During the month he was there, he was most impressed by the fact that every household in the country had a priest or a monk visit them every day. He felt that if these priests and monks knew a little bit more about hygiene and nutrition, they would be able to help their people significantly.

He talked to his physician friends and, although they felt it was a good idea, it would have to be presented to the Great High Lama. Carl made the appointment and described it like being in Shangri-la, going through gardens and trellises and arches, higher and higher, until they came to a door. As they went through the door, he was told to prostrate himself and move forward toward a dais on which there was a seated being of an undetermined age.

Carl said his body was there, but it was as if he was not. They stayed prone for a long period of time and then, suddenly, the Great High Lama was back in his body and fully animated. He spoke to Carl and said he hoped he was having a good visit. But then he said, "You have a question." Carl presented the lama with his idea for the people. The lama said, "That's a good idea. I will have to take it to meditation." In an instant he was gone again, although his body remained seated on the dais.

Carl told us that this time the lama was gone a really long time before he suddenly returned to his body again and said, "I have looked at the past, and I have looked at the future, and I have taken this into consideration. It is a very good idea, but the timing is wrong. Right now the forces of evil are mustering to enter the Earth. If I took one of my priests or monks away from his primary job, which is spiritual, and gave him a physical job, there would be an opening in the universe that would allow the forces of evil to enter. I cannot do it right now." Carl said, "Thank you very much," and they left. This was 1962, mind you, before Martin Luther King and John F. Kennedy were killed. About fifteen years later they were able to do what Carl had suggested.

When I have told this story, people have responded to me, "I can do as the lama suggests. I can pray for other people, and I know that is helpful." I say to them, "I would like you on my team because I'm out in the world doing things all the time. But, to have someone like you, who could keep me in your prayers along with other people – this would be a most helpful thing. One woman understood and said, "Particularly right now, with the world situation being what it is. I can see how my prayers could be very, very important in bringing about a healthier condition in our world and world peace."

One of the best things we can do for ourselves is to fall asleep with a prayer in our minds, or a song of praise or something that allows our soul to move from the conscious into the unconscious carrying with it a healing, living thought. When this happens, we are tapping into that divine part of ourselves which truly allows rest to be recuperative and healing.

Having done this one night, I awakened the next morning with a blessing: "May you have an uninterrupted day." I thought, "That is interesting." It became very clear to me that this was a very profound blessing because it allowed me to start my day with a sense of being blessed and in that space of attunement that is part of my soul connection with my divine self. If I have an uninterrupted day, it means that I can stay connected with the physician within me. And, no matter what happens during the day, I will be still in that consciousness. I will truly not take into myself the difficulties and the trials that I might have to face and will not let them interrupt my day.

The bedroom is also the place where we symbolically need to take care of ourselves. No one else can lie down for us. No one else can sleep for us. There are certain things that we have to do for ourselves, and, when we neglect ourselves, we truly cannot help others. In other words, we need to take responsibility for ourselves. We need to treasure and respect this magnificent body in which we dwell. It is truly a temple of the living God. In the words of my eldest daughter, Analea, it is "my body, my beloved."

Dreams also play an important part in our house of Living Medicine. It is in the bedroom where we most often encounter our unconscious self in dreams. We spend much of our life sleeping. As we sleep, our unconscious mind has the opportunity to help us with healing and rejuvenation. Also, through dreams, we can communicate with the deeper parts of ourselves.

To not address dreams in a book about Living Medicine would be like trying to talk about a life without sleep. Dreams provide a fascinating way in which we can learn more about ourselves in an honest, safe way. I have found them to be tremendously helpful in working with patients, both in understanding what they are going through and in evolving therapeutic protocols and modalities that they can bring forth from their own contact with the physician within themselves.

The subject of dreams is far too complicated and vast to be dealt with adequately in this book. Suffice it to say, the study of our dreams and those of the people we want to help is one of the most profoundly therapeutic and easily accessible tools that we, as physicians or people in the health care field, can work with. It is important to understand that a person may need some help in interpreting dreams. But, in reality, they are the only ones who can truly interpret their own dreams. We are there to help them. A few examples can be helpful.

A patient came to my office with a cold, and I suggested that she increase her intake of vitamin C. She called me the next morning to share a dream. In the dream, she was approaching her home carrying two bags of carrots. Just as she got to the door, a rotten lemon rolled off the roof of her house and landed in the bag of carrots. What that dream told me was that she needed more vitamin A instead of additional vitamin C.

Another patient, who had struggled with depression all his life and considered suicide a number of times, also shared a dream with me. He dreamt that he was standing on a rooftop that extended as far as he could see into the horizon with chimneys on top of it. All kinds of chimneys – thin ones, fat ones, ornate ones, plain ones, brick ones, stone ones – and every one was different. No two were alike, and every so often there was one that was incomplete. Right before him stood a chimney that was incomplete. In the dream he knew that these chimneys represented people's lifetimes and that, if he did not complete this particular chimney in this lifetime, it would never, ever, ever be completed. As a result of that dream, he has never considered suicide again. He still struggles with depression, but he will not shorten his life.

I had a patient who was a retired schoolteacher complete one of our programs. She had never been married and therefore always felt incomplete because she had never really experienced love. One night she had a physical experience that was probably connected with a dream even though she didn't recall it. She wakened with the front of her pajama top soaked with sweat. She got up, changed her pajamas, went back to sleep and woke up with the sheets all around her soaked with sweat while her pajama tops remained dry. She wondered what this experience meant.

As we talked about it, I made a comparison of the fourth chakra, or the thymus, to her pajama top that covered the area of her body being affected. She looked at me and said, "Oh, that's the love center." As we discussed it further, I asked her if she remembered the Bible story about Gideon. She said, as a matter of fact, she did. It was one of the stories that she used to teach her Sunday school class and one that she remembered from childhood.

The story of Gideon relates that God called Gideon to lead the Israelites in an attack on the Philistines. Gideon did not want to do it and argued with God and finally said, "I don't even know if it's truly you, God, who is speaking to me, so give me a sign." He told God he would put a sheepskin outside his tent that night and in the morning he wanted the sheepskin to be soaking wet with dew, but the ground all around it to be dry. When he woke and looked outside his tent, the sheepskin was wet and the ground was dry.

He still did not believe that it was God talking to him so he said, "Now, tonight, I want the opposite. I want the ground all around the sheepskin to be wet and the sheepskin to be dry." In the morning, that's the way it was. So he finally got the message that God was truly speaking to him and he did what he was told.

As Patty, the schoolteacher, talked about this, she said, "You know, I think I get the message. All my life I have been loved by students, their parents, my family and my friends. I have been surrounded by love but, because I was never married, I thought that I had not been loved. So I didn't understand that my life was really full of love and complete." This dream experience brought that message to her in a way that nothing else had been able to do.

One day I was shopping at the supermarket and, just as I pushed my cart through the door, the screen door slammed shut on my right hand. I stood there for a while because it hurt. I was shaking my hand and watching a bruise grow on the back of it. I thought nothing more about it until, a few days later, when a pregnant patient of mine was in my office and said, "What happened to you about two o'clock on Tuesday afternoon?" I replied, "Oh, nothing," and she said, "I know something happened." I explained what happened to my hand. She said, "Well, that must have been what happened." Then she told me this story.

She was taking a nap and had a dream in which she saw me driving my car down the road and turning at the corner where the supermarket is located. Just as I turned the corner, a car sped through a red light, hit my car on the right side and hurt me very badly. She awakened, frightened and began to pray for several minutes until the feeling finally left, her heart rate slowed, and she was able to settle down. When she told me this, we realized that her prayers probably intervened for me. I believe that if I had not gotten bruised and been standing there shaking my hand for a few minutes, I probably would have gotten into my car and been at that intersection at the time when the car went through the light. I truly believe that her prayers saved me from some severe trauma.

Irene Hotten lived in Arvin, California, with her husband, Mayo, who was a doctor. One day, when she was helping her husband in his office, a woman who was an itinerant worker in the nearby fields came into the office. When she saw Irene, she said, "Oh my, you are the woman," and then proceeded to tell Irene the following story.

Six weeks prior to that time, she had been out in the field working and had fallen and fractured her ankle at dusk. She had no family or friends in the area and managed to get herself into her room and up onto her bed. She was in a great deal of pain. Wondering what she should do, she began to pray for help. Suddenly, there was a woman standing at the foot of her bed. She looked at her clock and noticed it was eleven o'clock. This woman who had come in reached down, picked her ankle up, set the bones in the ankle and laid it back down on the bed. As the patient's pain eased, the other woman left.

Six weeks later, the patient went to Dr. Hotten's office for an X-ray to see if the bones had been properly aligned. They, of course, were. The fascinating aspect of this story is that every evening, when Irene did her meditation just about eleven o'clock, she would pray for those who had no one to pray for them. In reality and on an actual physical level, she was used to help this woman who was also praying for help.

Both of the last two stories about dream experiences that were connected with actual physical healings took place in the bedroom. Metaphorically, the bedroom is that place to which we can retire so that healing can take place. Both of these women were in an area of their consciousness that is similar to the bedroom in that it allows them to remain in that state of awareness in which the body, mind and spirit are so in tune with each other that healing can happen on all levels. Any time we move into a space of true healing, it is similar to settling into our bedroom consciousness. The external cares are quieted and even removed as the "at-one-ment," or attunement, takes place and we can allow healing to happen for ourselves and for those for whom we pray.

The bedroom is the place where the physician within can contact the physician on the outside in a very profound and comfortable way. When I was making house calls, some of the tenderest moments with patients occurred at their bedside. This holds true when we are at the bedside of patients in the hospital. This also happens when patients come into my office and we share that still, quiet place symbolized by the bedroom.

The bedroom becomes a place in our lives where our unconscious and our conscious meet – where transitions happen; where our conscious awareness of the connection between body, mind and spirit is very real; and where we move in and out of our conscious reality.

Chapter Seven

The Playroom

The house of Living Medicine would be incomplete without a playroom. One of the most important aspects of maintaining a healthy life is balance. Balance between work and play is pivotal to the proper movement of life energy. By play I mean that which brings joy and laughter, as well as relaxation and being physically involved with the living energy of spirit that enlivens us all. Play can involve others or can be an individual and personal activity. Setting aside a place for this not only validates it, but affirms on a material level this is as important as any other room in the house.

When the children of Israel received the Ten Commandments, one of them was: "Remember the Sabbath Day to keep it holy. Six days shalt thou labor and do all thy work: but the seventh day is the Sabbath of the Lord thy God: in it thou shalt not do any work." The Sabbath symbolizes the importance of taking time away from our "work." And, in the context of the Ten Commandments, we should dedicate one out of seven days to the enjoyment of life and the movement of the spirit within us.

Perhaps we, in this day and age, cannot find a whole day every week to which we can dedicate this type of time. But we certainly can understand the importance of taking time each day to allow our body, mind and spirit time to just enjoy each other.

Playing enriches our lives. We have become very aware that exercise is important for the proper functioning of the body. Exercise in any form that does not overextend our abilities is effective and important to our well-being. I believe that we need to find the type of exercise that we, as individuals, truly enjoy. When we do this, it becomes a healing activity. If the exercise is either boring or too hard, it becomes difficult and we tend to avoid it or dislike it. It becomes more like work. The more we look for and find ways in which we can exercise our bodies, which allows us to exercise our mind and spirit, the more this becomes a truly healing activity that is also play.

Our form of play may be quilting, knitting, gardening, listening to music, dancing, playing family games or even watching television. We have untold numbers of ways in which we can be entertained. There is nothing wrong with this as long as it isn't our only form of play. If it requires something from the outside to stimulate our life force, we become dependent on outer stimulation to keep us engaged in life.

For some, a form of play has manifested in redesigning their bodies. For many years I have seen an increase in the amount of body mutilation that people are inflicting on themselves – piercing, tattoos and excessive plastic surgery. I have wondered what the people involved in this activity are looking for and what they are missing. My thinking has not been in the form of condemnation but of trying to understand what that particular person wants to express.

We have for many years given our young people so much in fulfilling their desires through video games, movies and all types of sensory stimuli. I wonder if it has resulted in a situation of sensory overload so they cannot really "feel" and have to go beyond the "normal" sensory input. Perhaps, by piercing their tongue, they are trying to say something that they cannot express or feel adequately. Perhaps, by having multiple piercings in their ears, they are trying to hear something that goes beyond what they have been listening to.

In wondering about this situation, I came across an article by Larry Dossey, M.D., in the November-December 2003 issue of *Alternative Therapy.* I believe his article, "Living Dangerously, Risk Taking and Health" offers a thought- provoking and important piece of literature in understanding what is happening in this world. He writes: "The eternal job of the writer is to comfort the afflicted and afflict the comfortable." He goes on to describe our human need for stretching beyond our comfort zone and puts it into the context of our basic, innate nature, which is to allow risk in our lives.

In his article, Dossey said, "The grail quest is a symbolic journey, toward a psychological awakening and enlightenment. It champions and celebrates risk. It teaches us that a quest without it is not genuine, but is an exercise in self-indulgence."

We, as parents, naturally want to remove danger from our children's lives and this is commendable. But, how are our children going to learn to ride a bicycle if we do not put them on it and let them fall? How can we possibly create a risk-free world without damaging that inner urge that needs to be expressed?

Dossey wrote, "We have created diagnostic categories for rambunctious, risk-loving boys and have taken to rationalizing boyish behavior out of existence. We prefer, instead, perfectly behaved, undisruptive kids who grow up to be mellow, smoothed-out adults who are properly horrified by unsafe behavior in all of its forms."

Our desire to eliminate risk in our lives is an attempt to eliminate fear. And yet, in the very attempt to take fear away, we have created greater and greater fears. We compound our fears and do not transform them. The classic statement, "Why worry when you can pray?" is lost in a world of worries and fears that are constantly with us. "As politicians have learned, we are easy to scare, but impossible to unscare," Dossey said. I believe that the only way to deal with this worry and fear is not to try to eliminate it, but to face it, deal with it and move through it. This is the process of walking through and moving through fear and worry instead of avoiding it.

As I work with patients every day, I am constantly humbled by the magnificence of the human spirit as patients walk through their valley, whether it be a cancer or a broken home or death itself.

In medicine we have put up so many barriers and walls in the process of trying to avoid litigation that most physicians live in a constant state of fear, and their practice of medicine is directed by trying to avoid any risk. Dossey addresses this in his article:

"Many of us physicians remember when patients and physicians felt they were on the same side, and we wonder if things can ever be that way again. For that to happen, we shall need, I believe, to give up the fantasy that healthcare can be both effective and error-free and that risk can always be assigned to specific individuals.... In healthcare, risk and safety are like the opposite poles of the magnet, without which the magnet could not exist. Perhaps that's why nature seems to laugh at our attempts to eliminate risks completely.... Risk is a paradox, which has been defined as truth standing upside down to attract attention.... This paradox is our birthright – and a reminder that our obsession with creating a risk-free existence from the nursery to the crematory is folly."

I am not saying we should not be cautious and not take precautions. There is the aspect of awareness that we all crave and need, which pulls us past the safety zone of comfort and moves us into the reality of life itself. It is allowing ourselves to move into a life that enhances play and the joy of life.

One of the problems we are experiencing is addictions, whether it is to drugs, alcohol or video games. I have heard about video games that are so "real" that people get completely caught up in them. It then becomes hard for them to participate in real-life relationships. The person they can create in the game is something that they like and have power over. They also then have power over others. It is truly like a schizophrenic episode. Dreaming and daydreaming offer ways in which our creative energy flows and grows. But, when it becomes difficult getting out of the fantasy world and returning to the functional world, it is pathological.

We do not want creative children disrupting the classrooms, so we medicate them to keep them in line. We overwork our teachers, so they do not have the time or patience to help direct this energy, and we overcrowd the classrooms. We build schools with windows so small no one can see out! The great minds of our youth are either addicted to something or medicated, so they have trouble really allowing themselves to get truly zealous about any cause.

I heard many years ago that the way wars were won in the Middle East was that one country would get the soldiers of the enemy hooked on hashish. They then had no fight left in them, and the country was taken over. As individuals, it is only when we look honestly at our difficult places and our shadow side that we can truly feel the love and joy of our true nature.

Peace only results from dealing with conflict in an open, natural way and a willingness to look at all sides to deal rationally with the conflict. The only way we can have an abundant life is by allowing ourselves to truly live, not shying away from life or trying to sleep through it.

We can allow children to get hot, sweaty and dirty so they can experience how great a shower feels. Let them participate in other people's losses and hunger so they can know how blessed they are. Let them feel their own pain and loss and help them face it and grow through it. Some necessary medication is permissible, but it is not the first thing that we should use for relief. We help them take responsibility for their own healing. We cannot digest their life experiences for them; it is something they have to do for themselves.

As we give ourselves room in this house of Living Medicine for play, it is important to accept and realize the importance of unstructured play – taking time just to be and enjoy the essence of whatever is. Sometimes we get so caught up with the structure of our lives that we lose the spontaneity of unstructured or spontaneous play.

I still remember watching my son Bob as an eight-year-old boy in the back yard of our home, creating places for ants. He found an ant hill and was so fascinated with their activity that he decided he was going to help them build a community. This meant that he made pathways and bridges, sprinkling a little bit of food along the way and watching the ants follow the paths he had created. He would literally spend hours playing with the ants.

There should always be room for play in this house of Living Medicine, which means time to do nothing – nothing considered constructive – whatever that nothing might be for each individual. We criticize our children in school for day-dreaming and yet some of the most important concepts and life-changing experiences have resulted from it. It is such a natural process for us that we tend to discredit and downplay it.

When we create school buildings that have no windows for the children to look out of, we restrict their ability to day-dream. All children do not need to daydream. However, the ones that do can be really deprived of the growth of their spirit if we do not allow them to stretch and grow as they would if allowed to daydream.

There are multitudes of ways in which we could use the playroom – with little girls playing jacks and brothers wrestling with each other.

When I practiced medicine in Wellsville, Ohio, in the early fifties, my brother and his family lived about thirty-five miles away in Pennsylvania. One day I went to visit with my four children, including my son Carl, who was five years old. I had three sons and a daughter while my brother had three daughters.

When we got back from the visit, Carl was at his toy box, pulling his toys out and arranging them. I asked him what he was doing. His answer was, "Poor Uncle John. His kids don't have any toys at all. I'm finding the toys we can give to them." Now, of course, this was because all he saw at Uncle John's house were girls' toys and he was feeling very sorry for his cousins who just did not have trucks or balls or sticks or boy stuff.

I have thought about this story as a metaphor for a number of things in life. How often it is that we project our own needs and desires on other people when their needs and desires may be completely different. How often do we feel sorry for somebody and want to give them something from our compassionate heart that would be important and helpful to us but might be useless and maybe not appropriate at all for them? We project our own wishes and emotions and thoughts on other people because we feel they need them or they are lacking, But, in reality, they have not felt the lack or the need and have not asked for our opinion or even our pity. When we use our own desires to try to help someone else and do not listen to what they are saying, do not pay any attention to what their needs are or do not even try to understand where they are coming from, we frequently create more trouble than help.

My five-year-old son reached out to his cousins in a loving, tender way and, for this, I was grateful. However, I had to explain to him that his cousins really were not into trucks and that maybe there were some other things we could think about giving them rather than those that were so precious to him. I wonder how often we force our own precious ideologies and philosophies onto people for whom they are either useless or inappropriate.

The idea that we know what is best for other people because it would be best for us was brought forcefully to my attention in the early 1950s when I lived in Wellsville, Ohio. The business women in Wellsville and East Liverpool had formed an organization called The Quota Club, which had for its mission doing things in our hometowns that would be helpful for the people. We took on projects that were geared toward making the city a better place to live.

One of these projects included the health care and well-being of several old men, who were almost or completely blind and lived in shacks on the banks of the Ohio River. We felt that it was our duty to help these men improve their living conditions. We rented a house with enough rooms to accommodate everyone, hired a housekeeper, furnished the house with bedding and dishes and anything else we felt was necessary and then went down and talked to the men. We offered them this place to live, saying that we would take care of their housing since we felt they would do better in a different situation. We even took them to the house and showed them around. They were not enthusiastic and did not move into the house.

We waited a few days and then felt that the reason they had not accepted our offer was because they did not know how great it would be to have clean sheets and a nice place to live. So we went and bodily moved them to the house. They stayed there almost two weeks and then every one of them went back to their shacks by the riverside. We could not believe it. We were absolutely astonished that the offer that we had given them was totally rejected and that they could go back to the conditions that were, in our minds, unhealthy.

I have never forgotten this experience. It pointed out to me that there was a certain arrogance in my attitude. I had assumed that I knew what these men wanted and needed in their life situation instead of simply asking them what they wanted.

I think as a nation we have to be careful that we do not make these same types of assumptions in our dealings with other countries. Instead of trying to force upon them our idea of democracy, perhaps we should be asking what it is that they need. In helping people with their healing, we need to know their wishes or needs. The reason Future Generations, an organization started by my brother and his son, has been effective around the world is because they identify what the people themselves want, not what we think they should have.

We live in a world where taking time to slow down or just relax is sometimes very difficult. There is a story I heard when I was a child that has a great deal of meaning for me. It seems that one of my father's friends, a fellow missionary, was trekking back into the jungle with coolies carrying his equipment. After they had traveled for three days, he was all set and ready to go the next morning but the coolies remained sitting. He told them that they needed to move on, they had a schedule to meet, and so on, but they just sat there. He continued to try to persuade them and finally told the head man that he really needed to get them to continue with the trek. At this point the headman said, "Sahib, these men have left their souls behind for three days and they're waiting for them to catch up. They will not move until their souls have caught up."

Sometimes I wonder whether that can explain jetlag. And I wonder if the inability to understand ourselves and our fellow human beings has a great deal to do with the pace at which we live our lives. Perhaps, if we slowed down, our souls would catch up with us.

I think that we all should have a rocking chair where we just simply sit and rock, or a swing on which we can swing back and forth. This is very beneficial to our bodies physically. These movements promote circulation and help us work into our lives a rhythm that is part of the healing process. The gentle movement of the rocking chair or the swing serves to activate the lymphatic system. John F. Kennedy found great relief from his back pain by his use of his rocking chair. I think one of the reasons the elderly enjoy the rocking chair is because it allows a movement that is pleasant and soothing while it enhances the circulatory system. Babies respond to rocking from the moment they are born. This is understandable since, *in utero*, whenever a mother walks or moves, the baby feels a movement similar to that of being rocked.

The playroom can provide a place where beauty in any form can be appreciated. Beauty is different for each one of us. As we accept our own individuality, we become aware of ourselves and our own inner attunement. To put a time and place in our busy lives where we really do appreciate the beauty around us is essential to the growth of our spiritual nature.

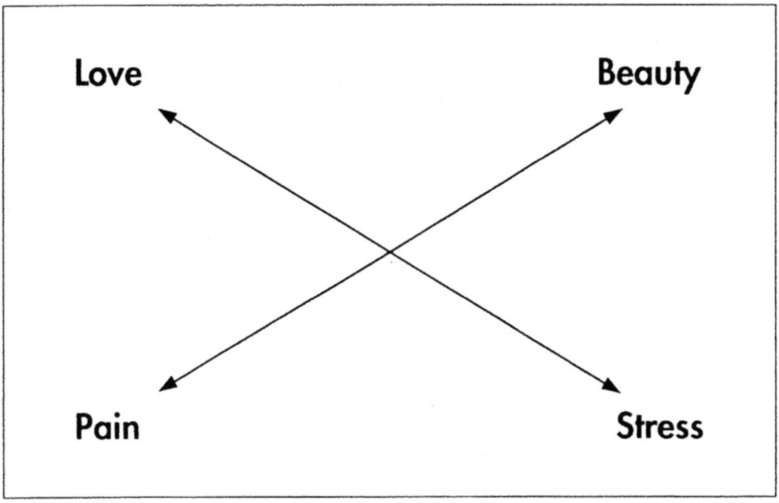

I had a patient who came into my office and relayed a dream, which she said she knew was very, very important and that I had to tell other people about it. In the dream, she saw a three-sided rectangle. The word "stress" sat in the lower right corner with the word "love" in the upper left corner, both connected by an arrow. The lower left corner had the word "pain" and the upper right corner had the word "beauty," also connected by an arrow. The bottom of the rectangle remained open.

When she told me this dream I really didn't know what to do with it. The following week I went to the symphony with a friend of mine who was having a great deal of back pain. The first two compositions did not seem to make a lot of difference, but the third one by Schubert affected her so deeply that all of the pain in her back was gone. Actually, she remained pain-free for some twelve hours. It was apparent that she connected beauty and pain. The beauty of the music, the involvement she was able achieve in the vibration, and the music itself helped her to transcend all pain.

Two weeks later, Mozart moved her out of her pain. The fact that the rectangle remained open at the bottom told me that this represented an individual experience. If people could move into whatever their appreciation of beauty was, it would help them transcend pain. This has been validated by the work of a group of harpists who play their instruments for terminally ill patients. Because of their music, patients have been able to cut back on the use of pain medications, particularly Oxyconton. Love is well-known to transcend us from our stress.

One of the benefits of using a castor oil pack is that it makes us slow down, allowing us to take time out to permit our physical body the privilege of using castor oil, which actually affects the cells of our body as well as our whole nervous system.

We are individually responsible for the health of each cell of our body. The nourishment we give ourselves on all levels – body, mind and spirit – is up to each one of us. This involves downtime or playtime. We are individually responsible for providing nutrients to the cells and removing wastes from them. Even with a blood transfusion, we have to get those red cells where they need to go. No one else can do that for us. It is the consciousness of the "me" that takes care of each cell.

A young boy named Timmy brought this to my attention. The first time he came into my office, I heard him before I saw him. He was not crying or screaming; he was just tearing the room apart. When I stepped into the examining room, I saw a young mother totally frustrated by her adorable five-year-old child. We were able to talk over the uproar about his health, which was basically excellent except for chronic constipation and frequent bouts of sore throats and earaches that required antibiotics. I tried to get a history of his diet and found that he consumed a great deal of sugar, milk and foods with preservatives. I suggested changes in his diet.

When he came into the office a month later, his activity was just as wild but he hadn't experienced a sore throat and his ears were a little better. However, his constipation remained severe, so I suggested to his mother that she start using a castor oil pack on his abdomen. Since he had trouble holding still, we decided to put the pack on from four to five o'clock in the afternoon while he watched a local television program for children. About a month later when he came into the office, I did not even know he was there. When I went into the examining room, he was quietly turning pages in a book. I was really delighted and amazed. His mother said that the castor oil packs had made all the difference.

She continued to use the castor oil pack as he started school. In the summertime, she discontinued them, but periodically he would come running in and say, "Mama, I need the pack; I need the pack." Throughout his school years there would be times when he would come home and tell his mother he needed the pack. It seems that he could feel when the tension began to build up in his system. He knew he would not be able to control it and that the castor oil pack would help. I have seen him in my office as a grown man with children of his own, perfectly capable of continuing his life and activities and raising a healthy family.

In our society there are many children who are on medications because of hyperactivity. These children learn that they can control their feelings and behavior with the use of pills and, sadly, many of them continue using other prescription drugs in their later years. How much better it would be if we could find ways to redirect their energy instead of just repressing it.

In the playroom we can also reconnect with concepts that result from nursery rhymes and fairytales. The field of conventional medicine could very readily be portrayed in the nursery rhyme: "There was an old woman who lived in a shoe. She had so many children, she didn't know what to do. She gave them some milk without any bread and whipped them all soundly and put them to bed."

The old woman lives in one shoe. She cannot walk, and she cannot move or go anywhere with just one shoe. We need to find another shoe before she can walk. Conventional medicine has moved into that type of consciousness and way of dealing with life issues. The old woman, or the ways of conventional medicine, is working very hard to keep all of the concepts within boundaries where they can be controlled.

Conventional medicine tries to understand and deal with all of the diseases that humankind is faced with. There are, however, so many children, or diseases, that it is impossible to control them. The old woman just does not know what to do; she is tired, angry and frustrated.

In the way it is being practiced, conventional medicine faces that same dilemma: It just does not know what to do. The old woman gives the children "some milk without any bread and whipped them all soundly and put them to bed." In medicine we treat the diseases the same way, administering therapies that are all right for symptoms but not for what is causing the problem.

We need more sustenance or deeper healing. We need some aspect of spirit or "bread of life." Because diseases do not act the way we would like them to, we "whip them all soundly and put them to bed." We control the disease by curing the symptoms not really healing it. We get the symptoms into submission by putting them to bed. We do not want to deal with the real causes of illness because we are so busy dealing with the diseases. Our challenge then becomes a never ending process of trying to quiet the symptoms.

There is another nursery rhyme that represents Living Medicine: "Mary had a little lamb whose fleece was white as snow, and everywhere that Mary went, that lamb was sure to go. It followed her to school one day which was against the rule. It made the children laugh and play to see a lamb at school."

Mary represents the healing, nurturing, feminine energy of medicine that is young and vibrant and very much alive, unlike the old woman. The little lamb represents the healing life force within each one of us – the physician within. That lamb is so full of life that it wants to laugh and play because it is bursting with its own living essence. It is also white, not contaminated. This lamb follows her into the school of life where all of the problems that the child faces (or the child within each of us), confronts us.

This can even occur in medical schools. Representing the young, vibrant, nurturing, feminine energy of medicine,

Mary counters the conventional way of dealing with disease. Because of how she plays with the lamb, issues are dealt with while diseases and problems are faced and not beaten into submission. They are worked with and understood in a joyful, creative way that makes the children laugh and play.

The Bible is filled with admonitions that we remain joyful and that laughter heals. A few years ago, I was really fussing at God about some things while driving my car. It was a time when I was trying to understand what was happening in my life. Suddenly, my mind was filled with the quotation: "This is the day the Lord has made. Let us rejoice and be glad in it." I said to myself, "That's right. I will be glad in it." I immediately knew that I had to change my license plate, which now reads BEGLAD. Every time I get into my car, I am reminded that it was not by chance that my parents named me Gladys and perhaps one of the most important things I can do this lifetime is to be glad.

After a trip to Japan where my daughter Analea and I spent time teaching, one of the things we experienced and talked about was the reality that laughter and a smile represents the one truly universal language. People may not understand the words we are saying, but they know and understand laughter. It brings all races together at a level that crosses all barriers. Our sense of humor may be different, but what laughter does for and to us is the same.

The healing power of laughter has been studied and proven to be a mighty force. Years ago, Linus Pawling did his personal research and found that he was able to overcome a terminal illness by simply watching comedy and laughing hour after hour. There have been many research projects done since that time.

We find that anger, resentment, fear and other negative emotions reside in the adrenals, which are located in the third chakra. But, at the same time, the adrenals represent a powerful center where forgiveness can transform these negative emotions into a positive force.

We know that the adrenals can be activated by physical jolting, such as the athletes do when they "pump their adrenals" by forcefully jolting the energy up along the back as their heels hit the ground. Hitler used this concept with his army when they marched and did the "goose step," a way of marching where their heels hit the ground in a forceful manner. Every time this happened, the soldier jolted his adrenals and activated the fighting spirit in himself. If a person is in competition or ready for battle, whether on the playing field or on an actual battlefield, the physical stimulation of the adrenals activates a physical process within the body and one becomes a better fighter.

When a person laughs, it is almost impossible to fight. Where pumping the adrenals activates the forceful aspect of the adrenals, laughter literally tickles the adrenals. As we laugh, our diaphragm bounces up and down. The adrenals, which sit directly underneath the diaphragm, get gently activated by a rhythmic pulsation, and the energy moves up from the adrenals into the heart chakra or the love center. When a person is laughing, it is impossible to march. With real hilarious laughter, it is almost impossible to stand up. With healing laughter, it is almost impossible not to forgive. Forgiveness and laughter go hand in hand and are the outcome of love.

So let us remember that, no matter how hard our lives are and how many difficulties we find ourselves in, these can and will be overcome if we allow ourselves to "rejoice in the Lord" and let laughter do its healing magic.

So let our play room in life be so filled with music of our choice – with beauty that we appreciate, laughter that stimulates and activates our life force and with the very loving essence of the healing heart.

Chapter Eight

The Bathroom

Assimilation and elimination in all aspects of our being are essential to life. In our house the bathroom is a place for cleansing, elimination, grooming and privacy. Every cell of our body needs to be able to assimilate nutrients, but if it is unable to eliminate the byproducts of its own metabolism, it will die. The taking in and giving back out is essential to the very living process.

In Israel, the Jordan River starts in the higher regions of Mount Hermon and comes down into the Sea of Galilee. Birds fly over the Sea of Galilee; people live and flowers grow around it; and fish live in it. It is a very living, active sea. This same water travels down the Jordan River and empties into the Dead Sea. Yet nothing lives in the Dead Sea. No one can live around it. Birds will not fly over it and plants do not grow around it. The only difference between the Sea of Galilee and the Dead Sea is that the latter has no way of eliminating or allowing the water to run off. It has no outlet. This, then, becomes the metaphor for the bathroom.

On a physical level, we can use the respiratory system as an example. We take oxygen in, but must be able to eliminate carbon dioxide. Anything that interferes with this process causes illness and, ultimately, death. In the alimentary canal, the food that passes has to be digested and processed and then eliminated. If anything interferes with this process, we become sick and we die. In the urinary track, the liquids that we take in are channeled through the kidneys and the urinary system, processed and then eliminated. Any interference with this process causes illness and death.

Another important piece of our physical structure is the lymphatic system. The body's lymph surrounds every cell and plays an essential part in delivering nutrients to each cell and removing the byproducts. Every cell of the body is surrounded by lymph. If too many byproducts and toxins accumulate in the lymphatic system impairing the natural intake and output, then the cells die.

One of the reasons castor oil is so effective in the healing process is that it is absorbed by the lymphatics of the skin, and carried to the deeper lymphatics, helping to keep the lymph clean. It is like rain in the mountains. The rain comes down between the rocks, goes into little rivulets, and then into pools, transferring into larger streams, rivers and, ultimately, out into the ocean. The lymphatic system is like that, and castor oil helps keep the lymph clean. So whatever else castor oil does, it certainly serves a vital role in the cleansing process associated with the lymphatic system. Although difficult to study in dead tissue, the importance of the lymphatic system is apparent now that we have instruments with which we can watch what happens to living cells..

Elimination at the level of the respiratory system is just as important. Whether we are awake or asleep, conscious or unconscious, as long as we are alive, we breathe. We can live longer without food or water than we can without breathing air. And yet, because it is so natural to us and so essential to life on this planet, most of us remain unaware of our breath. We breathe but we don't *breathe.*

Apparently, in God's scheme of things, breath was essential to humankind becoming a living being. So it seems reasonable that, as we become more conscious of our breath, we also become more conscious of our spiritual being-ness. Unfortunately, since we are so unaware of what it means to *really* breathe, we have allowed the air on this planet to become polluted, and we inhale all matter of substances that are not conducive to good health. All of the great religious disciplines have been aware of how important breath is, and they incorporate breathing in their physical disciplines.

The importance of breath is also evident in other disciplines. As I watched the great athletes in the summer Olympics, I noticed how aware they are of their breath and the control of it. They know that, to be in control of their body and their mind, breathing has to be coordinated and in tune with all of their actions.

When I was delivering babies, one of the first things we taught the mother-to-be was how to breathe with her contractions since it was vital to her and the baby. Each cell in our body requires oxygen to maintain its life. Cells die when deprived of oxygen. The baby needs the oxygen the mother breathes to ensure its proper growth during the pregnancy and during labor, when contractions are long and hard and the baby's need for this oxygen becomes significant.

If the mother does not get enough oxygen to the baby, there are problems. The mother also needs the oxygen in order to be able to maintain the muscle contractions during labor. On top of all this, the way she breathes and the consciousness she maintains as she breathes allows her to move into and through the pain of labor. The more control she has over her breathing, the more control she has over the labor itself. The progress of labor is enhanced by the way she breathes.

I have found in my practice of medicine that many of my patients, who suffer from various illnesses, including depression and fatigue, are unaware of their breathing – even to the extent that they hardly breathe at all. They use only the upper part of their lungs to make the exchange of air, which is just barely enough to allow them to survive. As I listen to their chest and ask them to breathe deeply, very often the breath sounds do not extend below the shoulder blades. This means that the exchange of oxygen occurs only in the upper part of the lungs. Therefore, the residual air in their lungs does not have a good oxygen-carbon dioxide exchange.

As we discuss their breathing, they become more aware of what it feels like to have a breath that goes deep into their lungs and to rid the lungs of accumulated residue air. They begin to feel better, and their health improves. Controlled breathing not only is a great stress reducer, but also allows oxygen to get to the brain and nervous system, as well as the muscular system of the body, greatly reducing muscle spasms and tension.

I suggest to my patients that they consciously – several times a day, for short periods of time – breathe in joy and breathe out fear; breathe in energy and breathe out fatigue; breathe in laughter and breathe out anger, etc. They consciously inhale into their physical being that quality of spirit they are looking for and consciously rid themselves of that negative aspect of their being that they are ready to release. I know of no disease process – whether it is physical, mental, or spiritual – that is not helped on its path toward healing by conscious breathing.

Breathing takes so little time; it is absolutely free; and it is readily available, no matter what physical condition a person is in. No one else can do it for us (unless we are on a respirator). I truly believe that if each one of us would do some active conscious breathing, this whole planet would be a better place in which to live.

In the urogenital system, when there is improper elimination, women can suffer from problems such as dysmenorrhea – a painful menstruation that is not a disease, is not fatal and does not affect all women. It is, however, a problem that, for hundreds of years, has caused severe pain and discomfort. Many women are unable to work from one to seven days a month because of pain and discomfort. For some women, it severely limits their ability to function.

When I started practicing medicine, very little was known to alleviate this condition. Some women were even given heavy narcotics in order to help them through it, and modern medicine has given us tools to help with the problem. Unfortunately, some medications completely stop all menstruation, and I am concerned about our interference with this natural process just for convenience sake.

The causes of dysmenorrhea are numerous. In young girls, an immature uterus, a small cervical opening, a retroverted or tilted uterus, or other structural problems with the female organs can contribute to the condition. Posture, nutritional deficiencies, trauma and psychological problems can also be causative factors. In older women, uterine fibroids, endometriosis, abdominal adhesions, pelvic inflammatory disease, ovarian tumors and bowel problems also have their affect.

Some doctors now realize that lack of good nutrition is a contributing factor, and young women who are trying to maintain an extremely thin body can have problems. On the other hand, obesity can also cause difficulties. Hormonal problems, such as hypothyroid, pituitary dysfunctions and adrenal insufficiency, can also represent factors.

A good, balanced diet with natural foods, plenty of fiber (which eliminates the tendency toward constipation), at least eight glasses of water daily, fruits and vegetables and moderate amounts of dairy products are helpful particularly around the period time. Exercise is extremely important. A woman who is sitting at a desk all day is more apt to have difficulty with her periods, partly because of lymphatic congestion in the pelvic area. Good exercise helps to diminish this – walking being one of the best, although bicycle riding, swimming and dancing are all helpful. Too much strenuous exercise can cause muscle strain and sprain and is not recommended. It is important to get enough rest and alleviate stress as much as possible.

Regular osteopathic or chiropractic adjustments, of course, make good sense since any neurological or muscular or structural dysfunction can agitate the condition. This is particularly true during menstruation, when the tissues are very sensitive. The use of the castor oil pack during this time provides a real pleasure. When women start experiencing menstrual discomfort, they can take the castor oil pack with the hot water bottle or heating pad, place it on their abdomen or on their back, depending on where the major discomfort is, and lie down, allowing themselves to relax. Frequently, the pain will ease off. The use of the castor oil pack for three consecutive days each week throughout the month can, in some women, eliminate the problem altogether.

Castor oil helps ease lymphatic congestion, venus stasis, muscle tension and inflammation. In my experience, women who have used the castor oil pack for small uterine fibroids frequently have been able to eliminate them completely, and some ovarian cysts have responded well to the castor oil pack.

Attitudes and emotions are very closely linked to dysmenorrhea. When a young girl is told to just "get over it" or tough it out, this can become a lifelong trauma. If some mild discomfort gets all of the attention she is looking for, this can represent a way of manipulation. However, I have found that the fear of impending pain that some women live with, month after month, can be devastating. If sexual abuse is part of the problem, it must be addressed.

Another critical issue is proper elimination from the kidneys to the bladder. Many people enjoy productive lives because medical intervention, such as kidney dialysis, is now available to us. Those of us who live in the desert become very aware of how important getting enough water into our systems is to our health. We know that people on chemotherapy for cancer do better if they can take in a huge amount of water. Like all other structures of the body, the proper functioning of the kidneys and bladder relies on assimilation and elimination.

The alimentary canal also depends on the proper intake and output of foods. As daily functions, we need to be able to take food in and also to eliminate it. We die if this process is not in balance. The more we physicians can help patients understand, in their own terms, the importance of this process, the more they are able to accept their role in keeping this vital aspect of their physiology functioning well.

It is just as important to keep the elimination going on the mental, emotional and spiritual level. Mentally, if we do not use what we have learned, it no longer serves us.

I know a registered nurse who has degrees in psychology and teaching certificates. She continually goes to school, learning more and more, but actually uses very little of her knowledge. In fact, when a subject is raised in conversational circles, she does not have a great deal to contribute. However, I have other friends who have only high school diplomas but who have used everything they learned. They understand the importance of "use it or lose it" in their lives, so they share their knowledge with people. When engaged in a conversation, they usually have something to say on almost any subject. Their knowledge is not stuck someplace in their mind but is accessible because they constantly use it.

On the emotional level, we are constantly being challenged to choose what is creative in our lives. We have available to us the choice between what is valuable or what is burdensome.

I found this to be true after my divorce. For a number of years the pain was so acute, and my involvement in the pain became a daily struggle. I worked on forgiveness, but it just did not seem accessible to me until I decided to move past the pain of betrayal and loss on to an awareness of what I really had.

I realized that I had enjoyed 46 years of a marriage that I considered fulfilling and loving. The work that we had done together, the children we had raised, the lives we had touched, the joy that we had shared and the experiences that we had created and developed were all available to me in my memory. My love for what had been was a living thing because it brought joy to my heart, a smile to my face and continued to enrich the life I was now living. I could look at my ex-husband in a loving way and thank him for giving me the opportunity to share his life. The process of forgiveness seemed a living thing, also, and although I still felt the pain of what "might have been," it was a bittersweet pain instead of a deadly, consuming one. I realized that the statement, "It's better to have loved and lost than never to have loved at all," had real depth and real truth to it.

A friend of mine shared a great lesson with me. She always thought that, when it came to love, she was a loser. Then she realized that everyone that she loved had enriched her life with a garden of varied and beautiful memories. When we choose life and let go of those things that have burdened us, we transform our existence.

In looking back on my life experiences, I have become aware that the ones I had that were hurtful and painful are now like scars that have healed over. They no longer hold the pain they had at the time they were created. I can look back and say, "Oh, that was a really hard and painful time," but I do not have the feeling of pain that accompanies that memory.

When I look back on my memories that were joyful and pleasant, I remember them and can feel the joy, love and excitement that went with them. The painful times left a scar, but the joyful times and the good times have become a living memory. They are still alive. They still bring me joy and hope.

Perhaps an indication of how we are progressing on this path of life is looking back and seeing which of our memories still have feelings associated with them. If we have painful memories that are still alive, it may be that it is like having an injury and continually picking at the scab so the injury does not heal. Whereas, if we can allow that injury to heal with time, it simply becomes a scar that we can run our finger over, remembering what it was and not having any painful feelings associated with it.

We can also understand this on a physical level. If we have an abscess, there is severe pain until it is drained. On an emotional level, if we try to hang onto the love of a person who has already moved on, the pain becomes that of a broken heart. On the mental level, if we have concepts of ideology or theology that no longer serve us as our knowledge grows and our understanding evolves, then the ensuing mental conflict can cause severe distress. On the spiritual level, if we try to hang onto our experience of God from the past that may have been an angry one, we can feel separated from God and our very living source. This becomes the dark night of the soul, but we can transform this darkness as we move through it into the light. We can experience a living, loving forgiving God, but we need to let go of the old. As long as this concept of an angry God was right for us, it was in the light. But when we moved on, it became dark like our shadow.

There is an old proverb that goes "As a man thinketh, so is he." Another wise saying is, "Thoughts are things." Yet another pivotal affirmation is: "Spirit is the life; mind is the builder; and physical is the result." If we hang onto thoughts and if we become so convinced that certain things are true, they become real in our physical body.

Years ago an eighty-four-year-old woman came into my office suffering from a severe respiratory problem. She greeted me with words, "I haven't seen a doctor for sixty-seven years. I don't like doctors, and you're not going to put me in the hospital." Well, that is an interesting way to be greeted by a patient and sets the boundaries very clearly. I accepted them and said, "Okay. Now what can I do for you?" She reported that she was having trouble breathing and experiencing chest pains. I listened to her chest and, sure enough, she had a full-blown pneumonia that could be treated medically, and I told her so.

In the process of listening to her chest, I found she had a mass in her left breast larger than a golf ball. When I touched it, I knew it was cancer. I asked her, "How long have you had this in your breast?" She replied, "Ten years." I said, "Oh really? What have you done about it?" She said, "Well, when I look at it and I see that it's growing, I say to it, 'Stop it!' and it stops for a while. And we go on, and it's just there, and nothing happens until it decides to grow again, and I tell it to stop it. I've been able to keep it at this size now for ten years. It doesn't hurt; it's just there."

So I said to her, "Have you ever thought about trying to make it go away?" Her response was, "No. How would I do that?" I explained some of the concepts of visualization and how when people visualize the white cells working with the cancer cells, they actually sometimes begin to kill the cancer cells and allow a healing process to start. She liked that. She is a woman whose body knew what she meant when she said, "Stop it!" And it stopped.

She left, and I did not see her for six months. When she returned, the lesion had reduced itself by a full centimeter. I said, "Wow! That's great. Now are you going to keep it up?" She said, "Yes." So, for another six months, she worked on it and came back in and it was still smaller. Then I did not see her for two years. And, when I did see her, it was the same size as it had been when I had seen her the last time.

I said, "What happened?" Her comment was, "Oh, I got tired of fussing with that old thing. You know, it's never going to kill me." And you know what? I knew that it never would. She and that cancer were living so comfortably together that it would never kill her. It would not dare! Someday she may trip and fall down the stairs and die, but she will not die from the cancer. There are many people who, when they die and their bodies are autopsied, are found to have cancers that they had lived with compatibly. Instead, they died of some totally unrelated problem.

I believe that we physicians have done a great disservice to our patients by telling them to check for lumps in their breasts every month. We even tell them how to do it. We diagram it for them and draw pictures of what they are looking for. Each month a woman is afraid to stand in front of her mirror looking at the beauty of her body, thanking God for the functionality of it, for the nurturing that comes from our breasts and for the comfort each one of us has received from our mothers' breasts. They have now become our enemy and we "check them for lumps."

I have patients who are afraid to touch their breasts for fear they will find lumps. I have other patients who check and check until they finally find one. It is as if the body says, "Oh, you're looking for lumps? Well, let me give you one or two." We have planted time bombs in our beautiful bodies so that instead of standing in front of our bathroom mirror and thanking God for this magnificent body that He has given us, no matter what its shape, we expect the worst.

Why can't we change that? Why can't we look at ourselves and recognize our breasts and say something like, "Hello, girls; how are you? Do you have a message for me?" We can check our breasts with appreciation. Approaching it this way, the body can let us know if there is an issue and, if it is one that needs to be dealt with, we will know it. Our bodies will tell us. The physician within each one of us knows what to look for, knows how to look for it and knows when it is time to be aware of it.

The bathroom is the place in the home where we really can make friends with our bodies, our minds and our spirits. The bathroom is also a place where we can take healthful, invigorating showers, wash our hair and wash away tension and stress.

If we have a bathroom where there is a bathtub, there are several things that will help us in balancing our body, mind and spirit. For people who suffer from arthritis, a hot Epsom salt bath can help rid their body of toxins.

Jet lag can be alleviated by putting a cup of Epsom salts and a cup of baking soda in a tub of warm water (not too hot but good and warm), lying down in it and staying there for fifteen minutes or so (without crossing over any part of your body, your legs or your arms, just lying flat in the water). Then when you get out of the bath, without crossing any part of your body, dry yourself off with the towel. Then get into bed. Rest or sleep for as long as you can even if it is just an hour or so before you have to get up and go on about your trip.

While hot baths are very helpful for some people in promoting relaxation and letting the muscles rejuvenate, for other people a shower is more helpful and may be more to their liking. Thus, the bathroom becomes a place where individual needs and preferences can be dealt with.

Sometimes the thing that moves us out of our comfort zone is one word, such as cancer or multiple sclerosis. Sometimes it is a relationship event, such as the death of a child or the death of a spouse or perhaps even a marriage in which someone moves in and we readjust and we accommodate. This can mean getting rid of some old furniture, moving some new ones in, or just shifting it around. Sometimes the furniture that we have had for many years, which we think looks fine and has served us well, may be having problems that we do not see.

As a child in India I remember times when a piece of furniture that we thought was just fine would be eaten away by termites from within. The whole piece of furniture would just crumble. We did not know what was going on inside because, on the surface, it looked good.

This could happen with relationships in which one person feels that everything is going along well and sees no problem. Then something happens, and the entire relationship crumbles because, in reality, it was not solid on the inside.

This also happens when a person goes into a hospital for surgery for something that might be considered a simple appendectomy. When the abdomen is opened up, they find cancer throughout. These things happen in life and, when they do, our option is to sit back and let that particular circumstance completely destroy all the rest of the good things that have been built in this house of Living Medicine. Or we can clean up the mess, replacing the furniture that has been destroyed or removed with something more useful and up-to-date.

As a final point, in the bathroom we have a mirror, and the mirror is how we see ourselves. This means that, in reality, what we see in the mirror is not the way other people see us. Rather, we see the reflection of ourselves. Other people see us through their eyes, which actually is a reflection of who and what they are. The looking glass that Alice in Wonderland went through in order to get to the deeper parts of herself is truly the mirror through which we see the world outside of ourselves, as well as that deeper part within ourselves.

A disease process that can be and should be diagnosed and treated from the outside can only truly be understood and healed as the inner aspect of us is brought forth and manifested. As we look into the mirror and see the reflection of what this disease process is saying to us, we begin to understand it in a way that an observer from the outside cannot or does not see it.

It is important to have both the inner and the outer perceptions of what is happening in our lives. One without the other is not complete. As we watch a small child or an animal look at and play with its reflection in a mirror, we begin to get a glimpse of how we, as evolving consciousness, can get to know and become acquainted with ourselves as we manifest on this dimension.

At this age, I look in the mirror and wonder who that old woman is because, internally, I do not feel like what I look like in the mirror – and yet I know that both the inner and the outer are real.

Chapter Nine

The Garden

Essential to our house of Living Medicine is our front and back yards, the garden and even the air that encircles our home. In addition to those elements surrounding our home, we need to recognize that what we allow into to our home also has a great impact upon us.

The front yard of our house of Living Medicine is what we present to the world. It is the focus of our life that the rest of the world sees, such as where we put our lights and Christmas decorations and the way others think we are. It is the house that they see.

Our back yard represents our unconscious mind and our unconscious being, where life goes on in ways that the rest of the world does not need to see unless we choose to let them.

As physicians, part of our job is recognizing that a patient who comes into our office initially presents us with their front yard, or what they want us to see or what they have created in the way of a façade for the world to see. That is fine because it gives us a sense of who they either think they are or who they want other people to think they are. If we truly want to work with healing instead of just curing, we need to be able to move into that person's back yard and see what has been stored there. We need to find what it is that sometimes even they do not want to look at, which may be the basis of the problem or the disease that has been created.

Frequently, a patient will come into my office complaining of a sore throat or a bad shoulder. If all I do is give them an antibiotic or a prescription for pain medicine, I have in essence done something with the front of the house in order to make it look and feel better. If we get into the back yard, we may find that the sore throat is there because this person has been trying to say something that they have not been able to say. They may have been "swallowing words" that they were unable to express, or they may have been screaming for attention for a long time and not getting any response. Whatever the core issue is that has been stored in the back yard when that is brought out and worked with, then the real healing can happen.

If the patient presented me with a sore shoulder, what we may find in the back yard is that they have been shouldering too much of the responsibility of the household, or they may have shouldered somebody else's cares. In the meantime, they may be carrying a purse that is too heavy or doing some physical things that need to be addressed.

One night, after I had spent three sleepless nights because of certain issues and problems that were manifesting in my life, I went to bed at ten o'clock. I finally dropped into a really deep sleep when I was suddenly awakened at midnight by a big thump as our indoor/outdoor cat jumped on my bed and began padding his way across the bed. I, of course, jumped out of bed and talked to him and tried to get him to leave but he would not. Instead, he climbed underneath my rocking chair, which has a skirt around the bottom, and stayed there. I tried coaxing him out and pushing him from behind, but he would not budge. When I tried to reach in and pull him out, he hissed at me. This went on for about an hour.

I finally decided to get back in bed and try to get some sleep since he was not about to move. I had just dozed off when he jumped back up on my bed. This time I got out of bed and grabbed him, told him he was symbolic of my fears and anxieties and tossed him out the back door. I locked it, realizing our huge, smart tomcat had figured out how to get in the back door, which we had forgotten to lock earlier in the evening because of all that was going on.

Every house of Living Medicine has some sort of a back door. The tents in which we lived when I was a child in the jungles had a back flap. Every house that I have ever lived in has a back door. The purpose for the back door, among other things, is that we can come and go without being noticed. If left improperly closed, we can have uninvited people enter our home. These can be actual persons or concepts or emotions or, as often happens, disease processes. Sometimes we do not know they are there but, when we do, we either ignore their presence or allow them to settle in.

The function of the back door became very clear to me when I was working with a friend of mine. As a counselor and a massage therapist, she has spent her life taking good care of her body and her life, as well as her friends and relatives. She is also totally devoted to her environment, including her garden and her pets. She adores her family, her parents, her siblings and her children. She grew up on health foods, understands how to use herbs, knows about essential oils, has used castor oil packs, has done biofeedback, knows the importance of meditation and prayer and is a person who has kept diaries and journals ever since she was a girl.

When she discovered a lump in her breast about a year ago, she used a castor oil pack and it went away for a while. When it came back, she did some visualization and active dietary changes, which helped. She continued with the loving care. When it got to the point that the lump did not respond, she increased her visualization and work with love of her body. In spite of that, the lump grew. She then began to feel guilty, thinking there must be something that she had not done or had done that created this. Because of her feelings of not wanting to disrupt the family's situation or her life that she had so carefully constructed, she continued to carry the pain herself. She finally realized she really needed help and spoke to a physician about it. Then she began the process of moving into the medical system in order to get the lump removed and followed up with chemotherapy.

We had in-depth conversations about what was going on. She said she felt like it was symbolic of her having let her teenage son bring his rowdy, disruptive friends in through the back door. In fact, since they were her son's friends, she took care of them. She made sure they had food, places to sleep, water and anything else they needed because she loved her son. Now they had taken over her house and were in the process of destroying it.

She said she felt that although she had loved and cared for her breasts she, in essence, was allowing the rowdy teenagers to destroy her house of Living Medicine. It was hard for her to say, "They have to get out. I have to get rid of something that I have created within my own body. I have created it because I have allowed cells that were not welcome in my body to grow and displace the healthy cells. They have left all of their toxic waste and debris all around and they have no respect for me and my house. It's time for them to go."

She then visualized the surgeon and the surgery as the sheriff coming in and evicting these young people. After they were gone, the chemotherapy represented the cleanup team that came in to clean up the mess they had left behind. In order for real healing to happen, she had to reestablish who owned the house, who was going to take care of it and who was truly responsible for it.

She became Athena, the warrior princess, who was able to get rid of the invading army. She stepped into the role of tough love where, in order to allow life to flow well in her home, she had to be discerning as to what she was going to have stay and what she was going to get rid of.

As we talked further, I realized that in my own life, while I was going through a very difficult divorce, one of the television shows that I watched was "Xena the Warrior Princess." I had no idea why I was watching that, but somehow it offered what I needed to identify with.

There are times in our lives when the living process requires a battle. There are times when we need to prune our trees or weed our garden. There are times when a tooth needs to be pulled or an abscess needs to be drained. There are times when an antibiotic is absolutely essential in order that life can go on.

We may have a back yard where a great deal of fun, joy and play is expressed. We may have a beautiful garden growing in our back yard that demonstrates rare beauty as well as a beautiful soul and spirit. However, this beauty will only truly manifest in a lasting way when we also choose to take care of Mother Earth.

I am very much concerned about our lack of concern for the renewable fuels in our world. The idea that we can keep draining oil from the Earth and that there is an endless supply is totally irresponsible and very dangerous. Oil is the Earth's lifeblood. As a physician, I am very aware of the importance of caring for our physical bodies. We really need to treat them with loving respect. We need to look at Mother Earth as a living body that has a limited supply of energy. Just as within our own bodies, if we exhaust our energy supply, we can no longer function. If we exhaust the energy supply that is available to us from Mother Earth, we will destroy her.

In 2000 I started driving a Honda Insight. I have never loved a car before, but my attachment and feelings about this car were surprising to me. I named it "Sylvia" since it is silver. The car was sleek and beautifully designed. It started with gas and then ran on electricity, without the need to plug it in or attach it to electrical outlets. I would drive up to a gas station like any other car and fill my tank with gas. The acceleration astounded me and I drove it as fast as the law allowed. I got fifty-seven miles per gallon.

Another aspect of the hybrid car is that it does not waste fuel when stopped in traffic. The engine just stops. When you take your foot off the clutch, it starts right up. I have never been left behind in traffic because of slow pick-up.

Since these vehicles are now available and other vehicles that use renewable fuel will be available in the near future, I feel it is our duty to Mother Earth, ourselves, our children, our grandchildren and our great-grandchildren to be responsible citizens who care for our resources.

What we are doing to our atmosphere surprises me. We have the information available to change this disastrous trend that we, as human beings, are allowing ourselves to be propelled into – a situation from which there is no return. Once the fossil fuels are used up, they are gone. At the same time, we have renewable energy sources that not only are available, but are also unlimited.

I have a friend who says, "It's time we stopped digging in the ground for oil in the Middle East and begin to dig for water for the people in Africa." Water is more precious than oil, and the continent of Africa is dying of thirst. Water does not pollute! We would serve our world better if we changed our focus from dead fossil fuels to water, which is in endless supply and is living. We cannot live without water, but we can live without oil.

We consider ourselves smart people and yet we do these really foolish things that not only jeopardize our health, but the health of future generations. It is time we stop polluting our world and begin, seriously, to take care of our beautiful Earth.

Our Native American brothers and sisters know how important it is to take care and respect Mother Earth. They know that it is important when a plant is cut to thank Mother Earth for giving us that plant. They thank her for fish from the streams and for animals from the woods. They use everything that they take from the Earth letting Mother Earth can renew her supply. We are totally dependent on Mother Earth and she is very accommodating to us, but we continue to take her for granted and cause her great pain. I believe, metaphorically, that we are causing osteoporosis for Mother Earth by continually removing minerals, coal and other substances that cannot be replaced. We need to learn to live in harmony with Mother Nature and be willing to learn the lessons that she so generously shares with us.

In earlier cultures when the feminine nature of our humanness was respected and predominant, we had an agrarian culture with no walls. People learned to live together, and they came and went. Fights or disagreements were carried out in the open.

When the masculine nature of our being became dominant, we created walls to keep people out. It became "us against them." We had to protect what was ours, and anything outside of the wall became an enemy. This ultimately resulted in the Dark Ages, where corruption and destruction happened within the walls and the whole growth cycle imploded upon itself.

We are moving into a new era where the feminine is reemerging and being respected for its nurturing nature and the acceptance that the feminine has within its being.

The day the Berlin Wall came down was one of the happiest in my life, with global excitement and the jubilation. It saddens me to see that walls are being re-created in many places. Not that walls are bad – there are times when they are necessary. It is what walls are used for and our reason for creating them that needs to be understood.

Walls can create a contained area where beauty and love and nature come together in a garden and create a sacred space. My little meditation garden represents one way in which I can express aspects of my being that otherwise I do not even recognize. It is a riot of color, with very little structure because I get very excited when a volunteer plant comes up. I even have some weeds that I consider very beautiful and have trouble pulling them out, although sometimes they need to be removed so the other plants have a chance to really grow and thrive. My garden is truly a way of expressing my own creative abilities and reflects who I am.

I have a great deal of respect for plants that show up in my garden as volunteers. About ten years ago, I noticed a little sprout coming up in my garden. I didn't know what it was, but it was pretty and so I just watched it grow. As it has continued to grow, it has become a tree just outside of my library window, with feathery leaves. It is a very pleasant tree and I have become very fond of it.

Through the years nobody seemed to know what this tree was. Then, two years ago, a friend of mine said, "Yes, that's a silk oak." I had never heard of a silk oak and thought, "Well, at least I have a name for it now." Interestingly enough, when I went to India in February 2005, I saw the same kind of tree growing all over the part of India where I grew up. I asked my friend Pavitra about this tree and she immediately replied that it was a silk oak. When I returned back home, I searched the Internet to find out more about silk oaks because I had never seen one in the Phoenix area. I found that it does grow in southern Arizona. Since it is developing right against my wall, my daughter Helene has been concerned that the roots would damage the foundation of my house. What I discovered was that the roots of the silk oak go very deep and can be planted next to a house since they do not affect the foundation in any way.

The amazing thing to me is that, for some reason, the powers that be allowed the seed for this tree to be planted in my little meditation garden. How that happened, I will never know. While I will never know where that seed came from, I marvel that it connects me to my birthplace – to the very soil of the countryside where I grew up.

Interestingly enough, I have a little hummingbird that loves to sit on one of the branches of this tree. In fact, as I write these words, I see it sitting there. The bird will stay there an hour at a time, just looking around and being beautiful in my little silk oak. To me this oak tree represents the wonderful connection that we have with Mother Earth and the amazing way nature will respond to us as we become aware of her and she becomes aware of us. What is it in my unconscious that called out to the silk oak the message that having this little tree grow in my garden would mean so much to me? I truly believe it is part of a promise that we are connected and that our needs are known and will always be answered.

I have a little papaya plant that I started from seed in a pot in my garden. It is growing very well and, at some point in time when its roots have stretched out far enough, I will take it out of the pot and put it in the ground so it can continue to grow. It would become rootbound in the pot and, ultimately, its growth would be restricted and it would probably die. When I put it in the ground and have it properly fertilized and cared for, it should grow into a tall papaya tree, producing fruit and seed that will then perpetuate the life of the papaya plant.

Our lives can be very much like this papaya plant in that we start out needing a protected space in which to grow and be nurtured. Then there comes a time when we are asked to reach beyond those boundaries, stretching our roots farther, so we can continue to grow and life can go on.

The pot for my little papaya plant represents walls that are sometimes needed in order for the plant to take root and grow. Children need to grow within the walls of a home until they are strong enough to move out. Our own thoughts and emotions need to have a safe place in which to grow and become strong so that we can recognize them for what they are and allow them to be part of our garden. We all need some boundaries so we can identify our own individuality and who we really are. Our personality develops and grows within these boundaries. We cannot live our whole life behind these walls.

There comes a time when, as the little plant needs to be taken out of the pot, we must step outside of our garden wall and meet the world. But, until then, our homes and classrooms should be safe places where we can grow and become strong enough so that we can then step out into the world.

I was talking to someone recently who was really upset about breaking up a friendship that she had thought was a life-long relationship. She said she was just not interested in superficial friendship since they are a waste of time and energy. We talked a long time about this and about how some casual relationships actually change people's lives. Often we do not even know it, just as the daisy has shallow roots and the oak has deep ones. Yet both have their special place in this world of ours and are important. The daisy has as much right to live in this world and bring beauty in spite of its superficial roots as does the oak, which has deep, deep roots.

Friendships are the plants that grow in our garden. They require care. They enrich our lives and bring us love.

Every house of Living Medicine has its own compost area, whether it is a pit or just scattered compost. And whether we are consciously aware of it or not, it is where the organic material is disposed of so that it can decompose and become living substance again. On a physical level, it is the actual organic materials that we throw away. On a mental level, it can be the thoughts and concepts that no longer serve us and are ready to be created in a different form. On the emotional level it, can represent the emotions we have become familiar with and have used and now are ready to let go of so that they can reemerge as aspects of our ever-growing soul. On a spiritual level, if there are ideologies and theologies that no longer serve us, we can let them go into the compost pit so that they can emerge as something that is truly life giving and healthy.

Out of the compost pit, then, grows the lotus. It is not necessary to go to the compost pit and pick up every banana peel or every eggshell and look at it and dissect it because Mother Nature understands and knows the importance of taking the materials that we give to her, physically, mentally and spiritually. She can recycle and reuse these in such a way that life presents an ongoing, continuous living cycle. Jesus said it this way in the fifteenth chapter of John: "My father is a gardener. Every barren branch of mine he cuts away and every fruiting branch he cleans to make it more fruitful still. This is my father's glory that you bear fruit and plenty."

During the last week of September 2001, I happened to turn on my television and saw the movie *To Sir, With Love # 2*. In this movie, Sidney Poitier comes into a rough and wild high school in the slums of Chicago. When he enters the classroom the first day, there is fighting and general chaos. He has to break up at least one of the fights in order to get any attention at all. One of the first things he does with the children in this classroom is ask them a question, one at a time: "Who are you?" As they replied with cocky answers about whom they thought they were, little by little, other children responded in negative ways since they saw that individual differently than they saw themselves.

It took time, but gradually these students began to really look at themselves and see who they were, which was quite different from the way they had seen themselves and the image they had portrayed to others. Each one of them had thought of themselves as losers. They had felt that there was no way out of the situation in which they found themselves except by fighting and rebelling. But, as they began to look within, they found talent and abilities they could access. The students realized that they really liked themselves and, by the time they graduated, many were no longer losers but genuine people who could contribute to society. They were changed.

On September 11, 2001, our world changed. The bombing of the twin towers forced us to look at ourselves and ask the questions: "Who are we?" and "Why do people hate us as Americans?"

I am finding person after person, when asked that question of themselves personally, realizing that they do not like themselves or what they are doing, and think of themselves as losers.

The attack on our homeland has shaken many of us to our core. We are saying, "There has to be more in me." Each country is made up of individuals. Each one of us is important, and what we think is important. If we think thoughts of hatred, those thoughts become part of us.

I heard a preacher say that if faced with a choice on how we respond to a situation, we start looking for answers. Then someone has to be right and someone has to be wrong. If, on the other hand, we recognize the situation and respond in a logical manner – taking into consideration all aspects of the situation – then hatred, which is anger gone blind, is not the motivating force. The choice we make can be a unifying instead of a divisive one. Then we are manifesting what we can do as individuals to help our country and the world.

"There has to be some way in which I can learn to love myself so that the rest of the world can love me." Our country is beginning to probe this concept and there is a change coming about from the individual to the national level. The war that we see manifesting on the outside is a war that has been going on within us. Now we are being forced to choose whether we are going to be losers or winners – not in winning the war, as such, against the people on the outside, but within ourselves.

Cayce's statement, "To know ourselves, to be ourselves, yet one with God," is our challenge now. Just like the papaya plant, we have come to a point where we need to be taken out of the restraining confines of the pot in which we have been growing. We must be planted in Mother Earth in such a way that we can extend our roots into the loving, caring world around us and grow into the reality of who we are, producing the fruit that comes from full, expanded, healthy living.

We are all well aware that plants transform carbon dioxide into oxygen, which is essential for our very existence. However, research is now showing that plants, by their very existence, can help us emotionally and spiritually. There are research projects that have taken a small plant into nursing homes, where the elderly are frequently depressed and unable to care for or respond to anyone or anything outside of themselves. If these folks are given a plant to take care of so they can see it grow and they can nurture it, many times their life takes on new meaning. A pet can also be very useful in therapy. If we surround ourselves with living things, our life is enriched abundantly.

In the Bible, the thirtieth chapter of Deuteronomy, verse 19, says, "I have set before you life and death, blessing and cursing: therefore choose life that both thou and thy seed may live." Every moment of every day we are making choices.

The garden in Living Medicine must, by its very nature, include the world outside of any walls so that the whole Earth becomes our garden. It becomes our Garden of Eden where we begin to think of the Earth as our responsibility and our involvement in life itself being part of what is going on in it. Then we can and will take responsibility for caring and loving the Earth.

It will require a level of understanding that we no longer can pollute our streams and our oceans with our refuse so that we are killing the water creatures. Matter does not disappear; it is transformed. When the pollutants we discard into our streams are transformed into toxic materials for the water creatures, we are causing severe harm to the whole Earth and to ourselves.

We need to be aware that we have a responsibility to keep the air that we breathe clean. The soil in which our plants grow is no longer nourishing when we put toxic materials in it that Mother Earth cannot transform into healthy substances. I am constantly amazed at the way in which nature has and does transform our pollutants. But there comes a tipping point where she can no longer tolerate this abuse and we who are causing it need to accept the responsibility and help with her healing. Just as in our own bodies, if we continually pollute them, there also comes a tipping point where natural and living forces can no longer heal this body of ours, and we die.

The house that Living Medicine builds must be built on living earth. It must have living water available to it, living air surrounding it, living plants embracing it, living animals visiting it, as well as living birds, with their songs and beauty gladdening the heart of the home, and even living insects to supply food for the birds. For us, as humans, to continue to live on this Earth, we have to keep her alive, treat her with respect, love her and stop destroying the very essence of who and what she is.

Chapter Ten

The Back Porch

When we step out of the back door, we step onto the back porch. Chairs and places to sit are arranged here especially so we can see what goes on in our back yard but also so we can watch the sunset.

Watching sunsets has been very important in my life, and in Arizona we have some of the most spectacular sunsets in the world. I was mentioning this to some friends one day and the response that I received was: "But that is when the evening news comes on." So, in keeping up with "the news," they were missing the grand color and light show of life. The evening news tells us about things that have happened during that day. It does not tell us about the precious moments that have filled our day, such as the sunset itself. If you don't look, you can't see, and you can miss the grandeur of life itself.

I remember as a child in India sitting in the porch swing on our back porch with my Aunt Bell. This was a clear early evening in the foothills of the Himalayan Mountains, and we were watching a glorious sunset. Aunt Bell asked me if I knew what the sunset was, and when I said no, she noted that this was a gift from God. That with each sunset, God opened a window into heaven and let us have a view of what it is like.

I was a mother with children of my own before I figured out what my concept of heaven was. I became aware that, when Jesus said "the kingdom of heaven is within you," he probably meant that we were creating our heaven here on Earth, day by day. Our thoughts, our emotions and the things that we do create the world we live in. We can put our attention on the things around us that bring a light and joy into the world or we can attend to what causes pain and hardship. It is our choice.

I have had glimpses of heaven in the face of the newborn baby; in the face of patients when they awakened to the reality that the physician within them is truly a part of themselves; sitting at a table surrounded by my children and grandchildren; and even kissing a boo-boo when my children hurt their knees. I have seen it in the face of Pavitra Masih in India as she cared for the children of leper parents. I have seen it in the faces of Afghani women when they learn something new about their own bodies and about birthing babies. And the windows were thrown wide open this past year when my daughter, Analea, died in my bed, with the whole family surrounding her with love.

Every new day offers me opportunities to glimpse this heavenly reality. And, as I watch sunsets, I am constantly reminded that it's part of my mission to attend to and recognize the beauty of each one. This is the reality of Living Medicine. It is our opportunity to look at what has been created and change that which needs to be changed.

The concepts of Living Medicine have become more and more important in the field of medicine as conventional practice moves deeper and deeper into the war against diseases. The literature that physicians are receiving now focuses on "pay for performance" activity in their practices and that of hospitals. Insurance companies have established certain criteria and parameters that need to be maintained for specific diseases, such as hypertension, in which the blood pressure must be held between 130 and 80. In diabetes, the blood sugar needs to fall below 100. In cholesterol, the total amount has to be kept below 180 while the HDL and LDL have to be balanced at a certain point.

When physicians are able to keep the majority of their patients (or at least a certain number of their patients) at these required levels, they can expect their income to increase. Hospitals are being told what medication they need to give the moment a person enters the emergency room with a cardiac episode. If the hospital follows this regimen very clearly, it will receive better payment.

Unfortunately, the requirements do not take into consideration the patients who do very, very poorly on certain medications prescribed to keep the blood sugar down or keep the cholesterol and blood pressure down. The mandated criteria and parameters do not take into consideration any individual variant which, of course, is part of treating a patient as an individual.

Drug companies have pushed hard so that certain drugs are almost mandated for treatment of certain disease processes. It does not give credence to the alternative therapeutic procedures such as biofeedback, exercise, diet and laughter. The focus is on medications. Many of these medications have iatrogenic consequences which then require another medication to correct the problem.

As long as conventional medicine travels down this road, there is no end to the problems constantly being created. Only when we take another approach to health and true healing will we be able to move out of the dark path on which we have embarked.

When we, as patients, begin to assume responsibility for our own health, we will have to make changes. Physically, we may need to change our diet, exercise or water intake. Mentally, we may need to change our attitudes and emotions while, spiritually, we may need to accept ourselves as spiritual beings. Only then will we be able to turn around and come back up out of the dark place toward which we have been heading.

As the house of Living Medicine is built, it becomes a personal individual dwelling place. It looks at and removes obstacles in our lives that have created problems through the years. It creates a solid foundation balancing science and art. It accepts into a living space the conditions in our life's journey that we have to deal with. It moves into the nurturing and nourishing of these aspects of ourselves and then moves deeper into our very core.

At this core, birth and death and the connection between the conscious and the unconscious mind truly dwell. Living Medicine accepts the reality that assimilation and elimination are essential to our health and well-being and that rest is important. It acknowledges that play is important in balancing our true living space and then looks at and identifies the way our dwelling place fits into our external environment.

This house of Living Medicine can be a tent or a million-dollar mansion. It is what each one of us chooses to create and build. Our house of Living Medicine does not neglect or back away from storms or difficult situations that arise in our lives, but looks at them for what they are in our experiences. It does not try to kill or destroy them, but allows our home to be furnished and decorated with the day-by-day, moment-by-moment experiences in life as they become part of our very cellular structure in this physical body and our eternal soul.

As we look at our dwelling place – our house of Living Medicine – we see that it has been built on solid ground. The foundation is good; it is balanced and true. Our house fits into the environment and is part of the neighborhood. It is a welcoming place, not a battleground. The grounds are well-cared for and it feels like home.

I have a lifelong friend who is in her later eighties and, in spite of the fact that her life has not been easy, she has built a home of Living Medicine for her dwelling place. It is light and airy and, although very small, is built ecologically correct. As a two-year-old she had hepatitis, which almost took her life, and then for many years suffered bouts of malaria. She had a learning disability yet, in her teenage years, moved to a different culture and adapted. Although school was hard for her, she did achieve an advanced degree.

Her pregnancies and deliveries were hard. She had mumps as an adult followed by mumps nephritis and ophritis and kidney stones. She survived a bout of cancer and a devastating divorce, through which she lost her business. In her home of Living Medicine, these are interesting art objects that are displayed according to what seems appropriate to her.

I like to go and visit her. If you ask her about her philosophy, she will tell you that she "lives in gratitude." Not that she has an attitude of gratitude, but that she lives in gratitude. There are many times when her finances are so low that she has to borrow money in order to pay her bills, but she sees this as a passing thing. Life, she says, has been good to her, and life is still good.

Each one of us has built our own house of Living Medicine. No two are alike. We have used life's experiences, both painful and joyful, to give each its own character. Even those of us who are in our eighties are still building because it is a living thing. Being a living thing, it will always find new materials with which to build. These materials come from many sources, one of which has evolved from stem cell research. Stem cells are living cells that create life, not just kill disease. The diseases may be overcome by the growth of these stem cells because life does overcome death – just as light always overcomes darkness and the life of the soul goes on after the body dies.

If you ever have a chance to go to the Carlsbad Caverns in New Mexico, you will have an experience of light overcoming darkness. When you are in the deepest part of the cavern, the guide will turn off all the lights and the darkness will be as palpable as black velvet. When the guide strikes one match, the light from it is enough to dissipate all of the darkness.

In stem cell research we find that, with the proper placement and nourishment of a stem cell, all manner of tissues within the body can be regenerated and regrown. This is Living Medicine. It is working with the life force.

The first page of the September 1, 2006, edition of the Arizona Republic, featured an article about genetically altered cells that had helped bring men with metastatic melanoma back to health. Although it represents early research, it shows promise. From the point of view of Living Medicine, the following statement made in this article is relevant:

"It's not like chemotherapy or radiation where as soon as you're done, you're done," said Dr. Steven Wosenburg, lead researcher and the institute's surgery chief, "we're giving living cells which continue to grow and function in the body. We can take a normal cell from you or me or any patient and convert that cell into a cell that recognizes the cancer. After these

cells are grown they can then be injected into the patient and as living cells protect the body against the cancer cells."

This type of research takes the life force and enhances it so that life itself can overcome illness. With this in mind and the awareness that with our thoughts and our emotions we truly do create the body in which we live, we can look forward to healing at a deeper level that has to do with living, not killing.

Another form of working with Living Medicine is the work that Robert O. Becker did in the mid-eighties regenerating tissues. In his book *The Body Electric*, he explains and describes the regrowth of tissue, entire limbs and other body parts by using directed low-voltage electrical currents similar to the electricity that runs through each nerve in our body. This book, published in 1985, opened a whole field of energy medicine to the world. The use of life energy to recreate and regenerate tissue is so much stronger and so much more hopeful and promising than the conventional medical model, which focuses on killing.

One of the things about our house of Living Medicine is that we cannot just move out of it and build a new one – not in this lifetime, anyway. We have to use the structure we have created. While we can rebuild or redecorate, what has been created is the result of our own choices and decisions.

The people or thoughts and emotions that live in this house with us have helped build it. We are the ones responsible for how it has come together. We might move away for a while, as in dreams or altered states of consciousness, but what we have created is what we live with and, in reality, it is us. In looking at this structure then, we consider how karma and grace have helped to build it.

I remember a lecture given by Hugh Lynn Cayce many years ago entitled, *Where Karma Ends and Grace Begins.* He defined karma as our memory and grace as God's memory.

He said the concept that karma is just memory represents a profound statement. We humans remember good and bad, as well as our creative influences and destructive influences. God, being the essence of goodness, remembers the good. Goodness recreates itself, but badness or evil self-destructs.

If karma is memory, what it seems to be saying is that as we remember goodness, it moves us from the law of karma into the law of grace. As long as we remember the hard times – our weaknesses, the things that we have done wrong, or the way others have wronged us - we continue to feed bad karma. These thoughts continue the bad karma.

If we stop feeding the memories of the hurts and the pain that we have sustained, they no longer exist. Good karma has, within itself, the ability to create more goodness. The bad self-destructs; the good self-perpetuates.

Karma is the law of cause and effect and, if we look at this law as hardships to be faced, we continue to perpetuate a difficult and hard life. But if we can understand this really beautiful opportunity we have been given this lifetime to accentuate the manifestation of the fruits of the spirit – kindness, gentleness and mercy – we will bring peace within ourselves and among humankind.

Edgar Cayce says that a karmic debt is not karma between people or karma with individual people; rather, a karmic debt has to do with relationships with each other. It is we meeting ourselves in relationships with another person. If karma is memory, then we are working with our memory of our relationship with another person. A karmic debt is a one that we ourselves have that is being worked out between ourselves and another person. The thoughts are the food upon which the soul feeds. We can continually feed negative karma by the negative thoughts that we think, or we can constantly feed our soul with the good and creative and healthy thoughts that we think.

What we create in the Earth plane, we must meet in the Earth plain. Only those you love may hurt you. All personal relationships are part of a pattern, and we continually meet ourselves. Each soul pays for its own karma, not someone else's. These are statements which help us understand karma.

How can we change the law of karma into a law of grace? We come into this life with deep-seated karmic patterns. We may have created in past lives a tendency to be jealous, to be angry, to look for contention and strife or to be consumed by self-pity. We can change whatever our particular weakness is that we are born with. It takes hard work. It takes a lifetime of work to change these tendencies. It takes prayer, meditation, working with our thoughts and feelings and understanding our relationships. As we do this with God's help and as we move under the law of grace, these patterns become only urges within our being, not an all-consuming pattern. So the karmic drive simply becomes an urge.

If we create our relationships with constructive influences, we move under the law of grace. In order to do this, there are spiritual laws to follow. As we work with these disciplines and concepts with other people, we begin to move into and under the law of grace. All that you can know of the divine you must manifest in your relationship with others.

Edgar Cayce gave us seven steps on the path from karma to grace:

1. Choose according to your ideal. Setting an ideal is central to this work, and the ideal is on a physical, mental and spiritual level. It has to be living, which means that the steps toward that ideal can be and probably should be always changing. We need to identify our ideals and separate them from ideas. Ideas keep people apart; ideals bring people together.
2. Act according to our ideal in line with the spiritual laws that we as individuals know and understand. The only way we can make our ideals real is to do the best we know.
3. Be creative, in the little things that you do as well as the big things. Find different ways of expressing and doing the day-by-day actions.
4. Give up criticizing and condemning ourselves and others. As long as we feed our negative emotions, they grow. If we stop feeding them, they dissipate by themselves.
5. Be not hurt by harsh words. When somebody says something to us that we take as being harsh or critical, we can activate self-pity and self-condemnation. The harsh words can't hurt us unless we take them and let them hurt us.
6. Let peace enter into your life and the life of everyone that you meet. Pursue peace. Peace does not descend upon us. We can pray for peace and long for peace but if our actions do not create peace in our relationships with other people, there will be no peace. Only as our actions and our thoughts work with peace with fellow human beings will there be peace.
7. Forgive yourself and others as God forgives us.

Our house of Living Medicine is constantly being created out of the balance between karma and grace. This is the brick and mortar that holds the structure together. It is how we have lived our lives, how we have related to the world around us and within us and how this has manifested in the flesh of our very being, which is our body. Cells of our body not only carry our genetic code, but also our soul pattern. Each one of us is uniquely different and yet profoundly the same.

If those of us who are trained as physicians and those of us who are aware of the physician within us can allow our divine nature to manifest in such a way that light and life, joy and healing are energies that motivate us, then this divine energy can and will work with the hardships, the diseases, the pain and the problems we face in our lives so they are transformed into blessings and do not become our enemies. Even death itself is recognized as part of life.

There may be times when a piece of furniture, such as a couch, is worn out or no longer fits in the living room and should be removed. Similarly, a benign uterine fibroid or even a cancer could have grown and now is something that just simply needs to be removed. We, as physicians, can be helpful in taking out or getting rid of that particular structure.

There may be someone or something that has moved into our home and completely taken over and disrupted the functioning of the home. Metaphorically, this could be pain, cancer or some chronic illness. The role of the physician in this situation could be to help to remove that person or thing, possibly first sedating him or medicating him so that it could be removed, but also making sure that, when it is gone, there is not an empty space left in the house that then would attract the problem or something even worse back.

I was talking to a friend recently who said that she had been struggling with emotions she felt were the result of frequent hurts that she had been subjected to from other people. She told me her way of responding was to build up what she called "a hard heart," which again, in her words, "had made her heart become stone."

She had been thinking about this while hiking when she looked down and saw a stone on the ground that was perfectly heart-shaped. She picked it up and went through a ritual in which she built a little altar on the path she had been traveling. She then put the stone in the middle of that altar and did her prayer work, offering up the stone asking that her heart be softened. She prayed to be awakened to the compassion and love that she wanted in her life and had been afraid to allow in. When she finished, she went home feeling lighthearted and free.

The next morning, in her meditation, she worked with her guardian angel and said something about having placed the stone in a special place along the path. She began to describe the stone when the angel spoke to her and said, "If you want to, you can go back and pick that stone up again and let it be your heart. You can do that. You can do that at any time." In that moment the woman realized this was exactly what she had started to do. In her mind she had gone back to the path and picked up the stone, reliving the things she thought had created the hardness of her heart.

She grasped what her guardian angel was saying to her: "You can leave the stone where it is and go on with your life or you can go back and pick it up and continue to carry it with you as heart of stone. That's your choice." My friend left her stone on the path and continued with her life, awakened to compassion and love.

If we do not replace our negative thoughts with positive constructive ones, the negative ones just come back in.

As we live in this house of Living Medicine, there are times when we pull back from the world and it becomes a dwelling place of quiet and inspiration. It is the place where we draw from within ourselves the wisdom and the understanding to go on with life and where we derive the hope and strength to face what is going on in the world outside of us as we look at and strengthen the world inside of us. These times of withdrawal and inspiration can be caused by some painful event that has happened or because our soul is just saying, "I need time with me in this house and I will draw back from the outside activities."

There are times when our soul says that we are becoming too complacent and too content with the way things are and it's time for growth. In which case someone moves in with us who we have invited or not, and we have to find space for her. This can be a growth process because it requires finding new accommodations. This person could be a new concept, a new thought, a new theology, a new emotion or something that is not part of the house that we originally built. But it moves in and, at least for the time being, it is there. Our choice is to accommodate it, make it comfortable and make it useful, or to make the decision that it is no longer welcome and it is time for it to move out.

We may also grow because of some really traumatic event that possibly blows off the side of our house. When this happens, we have to adjust to whatever it is in the world around us that has imposed itself in our house. It becomes a time of crisis growth when we either pull back into a corner of our house and disappear, or we accept the challenge that comes from having this whole new dimension forced upon us. We can either rebuild the wall or reconstruct it in another way, or do whatever is necessary to accommodate situations that have imposed themselves on our lives. In this way, we grow as a result of the crisis.

There are other times when we grow because we have looked out and seen a vista. We have seen something that is so beautiful and so engaging that we know we have to open our windows to this thought, this dimension of consciousness. This awareness allows us to see beyond anything that we have comprehended before – vistas of land, air and sea or whatever it is that has opened itself to us. This is what we call grace.

This is how we can fill our lives with love and beauty. It may actually be because of some particular illness that we have been forced to stretch our vision beyond our restricted window space, and we find that the world is so much greater and so much more beautiful. Or perhaps the world out there is so needy and draws us to that need so that, in the process of dealing with and involving ourselves with the new view, a true healing takes place. It may be that the disease process itself is still a member of our household, but our life is so much broader because of it. Our life is so much more expanded and beautiful in spite of the hardships endured that we no longer are restrained and restricted by the four walls that we originally created.

There will be times when we will be drawn out into this new area of life, whether it is because of the very beauty of the new landscapes we see and a need to experience new vistas, or a need to be involved in some aspect of life that may be painful or difficult. As we venture out, the fact that we have our home base solid, our home in Living Medicine still there, allows us to stretch beyond the boundaries and grow because we know we can and will come back to home base.

In dealing with illness, as we move into areas of pain or areas of healing that are beyond anything that we have experienced before, the knowledge that we have our home where the physician within us dwells allows us to understand a perspective of healing that truly is from the inside out. Because of this perspective, the physician within us understands why the problems arose and the best way to work with the problems so that true healing can happen.

There are times when the problem is something that has come to stay and remains with the person the rest of their lives. Just as hospice has helped people deal with terminal illnesses, the house has to be refurbished in order to accommodate the dying process. This is part of that person's life and living story. There are times, also, when the disease is something that a person can so incorporate into their life that it enhances and makes them a stronger and better person, just as Franklin Delano Roosevelt was able to incorporate post polio-paralysis into his life and became a whole person. Some of the people who I know as whole beings are people who have a chronic long-term illness that they will never truly get over, and yet it has not stopped them from living their lives fully.

It is something like a tree which, when it is putting its roots down, comes to a huge rock. It has two options. One is to put all of its energy into breaking that rock apart and going through the rock. The other is to extend its roots around the rock and incorporate it into its root structure and then go deeper into the earth. This makes the tree more stable and solid and it is able to withstand the storms that come along. If it is blown over its beautiful root structure has the rock incorporated right into its very being. It is more beautiful for having the rock there. A chronic illness can be that rock and the tree's roots the healing life force that encompasses the obstruction and transforms it.

Then there comes a time when the soul needs to move out of that house or body and go on. It can be that the person has lived a few hours or ninety-nine years. She now gathers into her soul the experiences she will take with her into the future. The thoughts she has had, the emotions she has felt, the things she has done, the people she has seen and the relationships she has had – all of these are now part of her karmic pattern or part of her soul memory. She gathers this all together and then is ready to walk out of the front door and meet whoever or whatever is waiting for her as part of her future. This is called death, but life goes on. The structure or the body that is left behind is now an empty shell and, in Biblical terms, it is "dust to dust." Because there is no longer life within it, it will, because of its very nature, crumble and die.

My birthplace is Fatehgarh, India, and in these latter years of my life I find myself drawn back there quite frequently, not just to visit, but because I have work to do there. This is because the concept of Living Medicine is so real in my life, and I find that each day helps me to understand at a deeper level the true meaning of the concept.

My parents went to India in 1914, right in the middle of World War I. My oldest brother was three months old when they left New York to go to a land where they knew no one. They did not know the language; they did not know the customs; and I doubt they had ever met a person who was Indian. They went, in spite of fears and doubts that arose, knowing that there was work that needed to be done in India for which somehow they were qualified. They were both physicians and

India, as they understood it, needed the love and caring that physicians could bring to her. Their deeply abiding faith in a loving compassionate God carried them across the Atlantic Ocean where German submarines were infesting the waters to a life that was to become a shining example of true love and commitment for their children and the countless lives that they touched. Their lives, for me, manifested the reality of Living Medicine. Not once did they become the many diseases that they lived through. These included sunstroke, amoebic dysentery, smallpox, malaria, malnutrition, abscesses and a host of other problems. They faced each difficulty knowing that it was part of their life's journey and, with God's help and a love for life and their fellow human beings, they would get through these difficult times.

When they began the work with the children of leper parents, they offered them a home filled with love and understanding so that each one of them was moved out of "becoming a leper" (that is becoming the disease itself). They became real people who worked as accountants, nurses, teachers, doctors, ministers, drivers, farmers and whatever else they, as individuals, chose as their life work.

Then I think about India herself. This land of my birth, this magnificent part of our whole world, for countless centuries has been invaded and conquered, with her riches stolen and her lands confiscated. Yet she still lives. Perhaps it is like a disease process that moves into a body so that sometimes it seems like all is lost. Then the thymus gland, with its reticular endothelial system, awakens the healing life force, which is love and out of which some of the darkest times of a person's life true beauty emerges. In India, when the Mogul kings came and conquered the whole country, the essence of India itself was activated from within. These kings activated their own creative energy and love so that some of the most beautiful structures in the world were created by the great Khans.

Ultimately, Shah Jahan built the Taj Mahal for Mumtaz Mahal, which is the most perfect example of true love in physical form. The Taj Mahal, in all of her beauty, reveals to me that she is a woman in labor. The magnificent dome is the uterus as it contracts. On either side are the breasts and the four phallic symbols stand guard. The great entrance is the opening through which the baby is born in a flood of water. How wonderful it was that I was at the Taj Mahal at sunrise on my eightieth birthday and then, again, this last year with some of my children and grandchildren, since my mother went into labor with me at the Taj Mahal!

The ebb and flow of life that is Living Medicine has been beautifully laid out as I have been blessed with the opportunity of living this life.

My daughter-in-law, Dr. Barbara McGarey, wrote the following reflections when she returned home from our journey to India:

Dancing on the Edge of the World

Landaur villa is as exotic and beautiful as the name may sound. It is a bungalow perched, literally, on the edge of the mountain. From its porch, which extends around it, you can see all of the Hill Station of Mussoorie. At 7,000 you are truly in the clouds. To the East, rising above the mists of the mountain valleys, the high Himalayas. Their ridges at a great distance in another country still dominate the sky as you look East. What an amazing awesome view.

Did we dance there? Not in the literal sense of the word, dance. But we stood there with Gladys and Margaret and as they walked around their childhood home we heard story after story, Oh look! This is where.... And this went on and on. Binding them to a time before and us to them and that time as well. We were blended into another place, Momma's desk and the table where they all sat and did their homework. The chest that had been in the living room was still there with dishes inside from another owner. It stood as it always had tucked in the corner such rich colored wood. All of this is so beautiful.

Then they stood and looked where they had played as girls with their brothers. "This is the tree, isn't it, where Dad hung the swing?" They looked up. We looked with them and saw across the branch a rusted piece of metal and links of a chain around it. The metal had been placed over the branch to protect it. It had. And the chain with four or five links on each side also rusted. But as we looked we saw it bright shining and young children gleeful around the base seeing the swing for the first time and taking turns to see who could swing out the farthest. It must have been a glorious swing that took them out over the patio and the house. They were girls then and in this moment are girls again.

So that was the dancing. Not a two-step or ballet but a dance of the heart unlike any other. OH look! Come see! This is where....

On this same trip my fifteen-year-old granddaughter wrote in the guest book at the children's home in Dhanari a heartfelt definition of Living Medicine:

> *In the paper you read about suffering in other continents. When I came to India, I saw it through the streets. Here at the children's home, I saw only smiling faces – I feel so blessed to have been here and meet you all. This is the greatest amount of happiness I've seen in a while, from people with very little but love. Thank you for everything! I can't wait to visit again and God bless you all!*
>
> Hannah and McGarey Family

In this house of Living Medicine, we will all step onto our own back porches and watch our loved ones create their own sunsets. And what we see of that sunset is our own personal experience. No two people experience a sunset in the same way. Just as no two people experience each other in the same way and none of us experience the same disease in the same way. Just so each sunset is different. We will all die and bring our life – our day on this Earth – to a close. Our challenge is to experience our lives with all of its joys and difficulties. When we die, we will not die of cancer but, like my daughter Analea said, after experiencing cancer.

William Sloan Coffin, in his wonderful book entitled *Credo*, has two quotes I would like to use:

"It's hope that helps us keep the faith, despite the evidence, knowing that only in doing so has the evidence any chance of changing."

"Martin Luther was right: 'God can carve the rotten wood and ride the lame horse.'"

With these two quotes in mind, I look at the future of medicine with great hope. The evidence that we are faced with is that of a broken system. The solutions for correcting the system are fragile and deal only with the symptoms and not the underlying sickness. When we look at the evidence that presents itself, we can become discouraged and continue to look for ways in which we could patch up the tears in the fabric of the system itself that leaves us vulnerable and still broken. However, with hope and faith, we have a chance to change the evidence and create a system that is whole and strong.

If God can carve the rotten wood and ride the lame horse then with divine help we can create a strong and loving health system. In order to do this we need to change our focus from killing and destroying to living and loving. The concept of Living Medicine gives us the opportunity to do this. We can take our God-given creative energy and focus it on life and use the tools that have evolved in the science of medicine to bring the spirit of love and hope and healing back into the practice of medicine.

CPSIA information can be obtained at www.ICGtesting.com
Printed in the USA
BVOW07s0646251114

376584BV00002B/10/P

9 780981 464893